# ELEMENTARY ALGEBRA REVIEW
## Third Edition

Ellen Freedman
Kelly A. Jackson
Virginia Licata
Barbara Jane Sparks

Camden County College

**McGraw-Hill Primis Custom Publishing**

New York  St. Louis  San Francisco  Auckland  Bogotá
Caracas  Lisbon  London  Madrid  Mexico  Milan  Montreal
New Delhi  Paris  San Juan  Singapore  Sydney  Tokyo  Toronto

**McGraw-Hill Higher Education**
A Division of The **McGraw-Hill** Companies

Elementary Algebra Review

McGraw-Hill's Primis Custom Series consists of products that are produced from camera-ready copy. Peer review, class testing, and accuracy are primarily the responsibility of the author(s).

3 4 5 6 7 8 9 0 QPD QPD 0 9 8 7 6 5 4 3 2

ISBN 0-07-251037-4

Sponsoring Editor: Constance Ditzel
Printer/Binder: Quebecor Printing Dubuque, Inc.

## ABOUT THE AUTHORS

Each of the authors brings a wealth of past experiences to the Basic Math program at Camden County College and through their combined efforts they have created a comprehensive review text to be used with any Elementary Algebra course.

Ellen Freedman earned a B.S. in Mathematics Education at Temple University and an M.A. in Learning Disabilities at Rowan College of New Jersey. Ellen taught high school mathematics in Philadelphia, and worked in industry as a computer systems analyst before settling in at Camden County College. She has taught basic skills mathematics at the college since 1988, including special sections for students with learning disabilities. She has given regional and national workshops on math anxiety, learning styles, teaching mathematics to college students with learning disabilities and how to incorporate technology and the Internet into the math classroom. She has won national awards for her use of multimedia and technology in the classroom. Ellen's math anxiety web site, www.mathpower.com has received numerous awards and is recommended by the The National Council of Teachers of Mathematics, The Australian Association of Mathematics Teachers and the Canadian Mathematical Society.

Kelly Jackson graduated from Franklin and Marshall College with a B.A.degree in Mathematics. She holds a Master's Degree in Community College Teaching with a Specialization in Mathematics from Rowan University and a Master's Degree in Educational Studies from the University of Delaware. She is currently ABD at the University of Delaware for a PhD in Measurement, Statistics and Evaluation. Kelly was hired as a fulltime faculty member in 1992. She is an Associate Professor, with a dual appointment in the Math Department and the Basic Skills Math Department. She is currently the chair of the Basic Skills Math Department. Kelly speaks regularly at workshops and conferences on topics such as: teaching math to students with learning disabilities, using the TI-83 calculator in a statistics classroom, and teaching math to students with hearing loss. She is fluent in American Sign Language, and teaches all of the developmental math courses offered at the Mid-Atlantic Post Secondary Center for the Deaf and Hard of Hearing,which is housed at the college.

Virginia Licata received a B.A. in Mathematics from St. Bonaventure University and an MATM from Villanova University. Ginny taught in high schools in Florida, New Jersey and New York from 1961 to 1980 when she joined Camden County College as Coordinator of Basic Math Skills. From 1986 to 1988, she also coordinated a large Challenge Grant, and during that time passing and retention rates in the math classrooms increased and a calculator experiment was introduced. Ginny is active in the Mathematics Association of Two Year Colleges of New Jersey, and she was an original member of the New Jersey Basic Skills Math Advisory Committee. In January of 1992 Ginny joined the ranks of Camden County College's Basic Skills Math faculty and served as the first chairman of the Math Skills Department.

Barbara Jane Sparks holds an A.A. from Salem Community College, a B.A. in Mathematics and a M.A. in Community College Education from Glassboro State College. In 1990 she joined Camden County College as the first full-time faculty member in the Basic Skills Math Program. During her twenty-one years as a full-time developmental mathematics instructor, she has taught at two New Jersey Community Colleges and at the University of Delaware. As a former non-traditional community college student, BJ is familiar with the academic needs of the adult learner. She has developed many unique and interesting ways to approach some of the more difficult topics in developmental mathematics, and continues to share her ideas with her students and colleagues through various workshops at the local and national level.

# Preface

This Elementary Algebra Review workbook is designed for use in any elementary algebra course or by any student needing to retrace typical elementary algebra problems. Upon completion of these review problems, the student should feel comfortable taking any entrance or placement test or final exam involving elementary algebra.

The objective of this workbook is not to provide instruction. Rather, it is a pool of carefully sequenced review problems for students to use when preparing for unit or cumulative tests (such as final exams). The material is split into eight units. Each unit contains at least two free response forms and one multiple choice form. There is also a comprehensive review which contains problems from all eight units. Answers are provided for all problems in this workbook, so students can check their answers.

This workbook has been used with remarkable success in a pre-college program that each year enrolls over 4,200 students in elementary algebra.

# Contents

# Elementary Algebra Review

# Unit 1

# Introduction to Algebra

**Write the following phrases using symbols.**

1. a. c decreased by 4          b. 7 less than x

2. a. 4 more than b          b. twice the difference of 3 and x

3. a. 8 minus x          b. the sum of 5 times x and y

4. a. 5 times the sum of x and y          b. the quotient when 6 minus y is divided by 7 minus y

5. a. the product of x, y, and z          b. the product of 3 and the sum of 2 more than x

6. a. 7 divided by x          b. the quotient of 6 and y

**Use the Distributive Property to remove parentheses.**

7. $5(3a + 4b)$          8. $a(2b + c)$          9. $3x(y + 4)$

**Use exponents to write the following.**

10. $3 \cdot 3 \cdot b \cdot b \cdot b \cdot b \cdot b$          11. $7 \cdot 7 \cdot 7 \cdot h \cdot h \cdot h \cdot h$

**Simplify the following expressions.**

12.    a. $9 - 3 \cdot 2$      b. $2 \cdot 3^3 - 1$      c. $4 - (5 - 4)^2 \cdot 3$      d. $16 - 4 \div 2$

**Evaluate the following expressions if x = 3 and y = 1.**

13.    a. $2x^2$      b. $(2x)^2$      c. $4x^2y^3$

**Evaluate the following algebraic expressions if x = 2, y = 3, and z = 1.**

14.　　a. $2xy - z$　　　　　b. $\dfrac{y + 2z}{4x}$　　　　c. $3(4y + z)$

**Evaluate.**

15. a. $-|5|$　　　　　b. $|-3|$　　　　　c. $-|-1|$

**Evaluate using the rules of signed numbers and the order of operations.**

16. a. $-14 + 24$　　　　b. $12 - 5$　　　　c. $-10 + 4$　　　　d. $-3 -(-1)$

17. a. $(-6) + 6$　　　　b. $(8) + (-9)$　　　c. $-8 + 8$　　　　d. $(-4) + (-6)$

18. a. $-7 - 3$　　　　b. $-11 + (-1)$　　c. $-19 - 6$　　　　d. $-15 - (-5)$

19. a. $(6) - (-4)$　　　b. $31 - 5$　　　　c. $-17 - (-4)$　　　d. $-23 - 14$

20. a. $-7 + 2 - 1$　　　b. $-3 + (-1) + 4$　　c. $6 - 2 + 5$　　　d. $4 + 8 - 2$

21. $-4 - (-2) - 4 + 1$　　b. $5 - (-3) + (-2)$　　c. $4 - (-3) - (-2)$　　d. $2 + (-1) - (-6)$

22. $-\dfrac{1}{2} + \dfrac{5}{7}$

23. $-4\dfrac{3}{4} - 5\dfrac{7}{12}$

24. $(.65) - (-.5)$

25. $(6)(-2)(0)(-3)$

26.　　a. $(-3)(5)$　　　b. $(-2)(-1)(-8)$　　　c. $(4)(-1)(2)(-3)$

27.  a.  $-3^2$        b.  $(-4)^2$           c.  $(-1)^3$

28.  a.  $\dfrac{-18}{-6}$        b.  $\dfrac{-30}{5}$           c.  $24 \div -8$

29.  a.  $\dfrac{0}{8}$        b.  $\dfrac{-7}{0}$           c.  $\dfrac{5}{-5}$

30.  a.  $-4 - (-1)(-2)$           b.  $12 \div 4 + 2$

31.  a.  $9 + 4(8 - 5)^2$           b.  $16 \div 2 - 6 \cdot 3$

32.  a.  $4 - 6 - (-3)$           b.  $3 - 2 + (-2)^2 \cdot 4$

33.  a.  $(-4)^2 - (-6)^2$           b.  $(-5)^2 - 3^2$

34.  $5 - 2(6 - 7)^3$

35.  $\dfrac{-15 - 9}{-10 + 4}$

36.  $\dfrac{2(-5) - (-3)^2}{2 + (-6)^2}$

**Evaluate if a = 3,  b = -2,  and c = 4.**

37.  $-3a - b^2$

38.  $\dfrac{4a - 2b}{ab - 3c}$

39.  $(a - b)^2$

4

**Perform the indicated operations.**

40.  a. $6x - 2x$  b. $3x - 2y - 8x - 6y$

41.  a. $2a^2 + 5 - a^2$  b. $6a^2 + 7b^2 - 3a^2 - 9b^2 + 5$

42.  a. $4ab + 3ab$  b. $4x^3 + 2x^2 - 6x - 7x^3 - 8x^2 + 3x$

43.  a. $12m^2n - 5m^2n$  b. $7a^2b^2 + 4a^2b^2$

44.  Subtract $2x^2$ from the sum of $4x^2$ and $7x^2$

45.  $9xy + 4ab - 3ab - 2xy$

46.  a. $(3a^2b^3c^4)(2ab^4c^2)$  b. $(3x^2)(-4x)$

47.  a. $(4x^2)(5x^4)$  b. $(2x^4y^5z)(7xyz^2)$

48.  a. $\dfrac{15a^6}{3a^4}$  b. $\dfrac{27x^3y^4}{9xy^3}$

49.  a. $\dfrac{15x^2}{x^2}$  b. $\dfrac{36x^5y^4z^3}{6x^4y^4z^2}$

50.  a. $(5x^2y^3)(3x^2y^3)$  b. $5x^2y^3 + 3x^2y^3$

# Unit 1
## Review Form B

**Write the following phrases using symbols.**

1. a. a times b

   b. the quotient of x and the sum of x and y

2. a. 8 less than x

   b. 5 minus x

3. a. 6 more than a

   b. three times the difference of c and d

4. a. 7 times the sum of x and y

   b. the sum of 7 times x and y

5. a. the product of 4, a, b, and c

   b. the product of 2 and the sum of r and s

6. the quotient when 3 more than x is divided by 3 decreased by x

**Use the Distributive Property to remove parentheses.**

7. $2(2x + 3y)$     8. $r(s + 2t)$     9. $3a(2 + b)$

**Use exponents to write the following.**

10. $4 \cdot 4 \cdot 4 \cdot k \cdot k \cdot k \cdot k \cdot k$     11. $7 \cdot 7 \cdot d \cdot d \cdot d \cdot e \cdot f \cdot f$

**Simplify the following expressions.**

12.   a. $10 - 4 \cdot 2$     b. $4 \cdot 2^3 + 6$     c. $2 + (4 - 1)^2 \cdot 3$     d. $15 - 6 \div 2$

**Evaluate the following expressions if x = 3 and y = 1.**

13.   a. $4x^2$     b. $(4x)^2$     c. $3x^2y^4$

**Evaluate the following algebraic expressions if a = 2, b = 3, and c = 1.**

14. a. $4ac + b$ 　　　　b. $\dfrac{b - a}{3c}$ 　　　　c. $2(6a - b)$

**Evaluate.**

15. a. $|-2|$ 　　　　b. $-|-6|$ 　　　　c. $-|4|$

**Evaluate using the rules of signed numbers and the order of operations.**

16. a. $-10 + 19$ 　　b. $17 - 10$ 　　c. $-6 + 7$ 　　d. $(-1) + (-9)$

17. a. $(-3) + 3$ 　　b. $-12 - 12$ 　　c. $6 + (-4)$ 　　d. $-7 + 11$

18. a. $-6 - 9$ 　　b. $-21 - 17$ 　　c. $-13 - (-6)$ 　　d. $(-4) - 6$

19. a. $(5) - (-2)$ 　　b. $14 + (-3)$ 　　c. $-6 + 0$ 　　d. $-(-7) + 3$

20. a. $-5 + 1 - 4$ 　　b. $-2 + (-5) + 3$ 　　c. $8 - 9 + 14$ 　　d. $6 - (-3) - 1$

21. a. $-1 + 3 - 2 - (-6)$ 　　b. $7 - (-4) + (-1)$ 　　c. $6 - (-3) - (-5)$ 　　d. $8 - (-2) + (-5)$

22. $\dfrac{-3}{4} + \dfrac{7}{8}$

23. $-2\dfrac{1}{2} - 3\dfrac{5}{6}$

24. $(.38) - (.3)$

25. $(4)(-1)(0)(2)$

26. a. $(-5)(8)$ 　　b. $(-2)(-3)(-4)$ 　　c. $(-1)(2)(-6)(3)$

27.    a.  $-2^2$        b.  $(-2)^2$            c.  $(-1)^5$

28.    a.  $\dfrac{-24}{4}$        b.  $\dfrac{-16}{-4}$           c.  $-36 \div -4$

29.    a.  $\dfrac{6}{0}$        b.  $\dfrac{0}{-3}$            c.  $6 \div -6$

30.  a.  $-2 - (-3)(-1)$           b.  $16 \div 8 - 6$

31.  a.  $6 + 3(7 - 5)^2$           b.  $-24 \div 3 + 4 \cdot 5$

32.  a.  $8 - 6 - (-2)$           b.  $5 - 3 + (-3)^2 \cdot 2$

33.  a.  $(-3)^2 - (-5)^2$        b.  $(-6)^2 - 4^2$

34.  $6 - 2(3 - 4)^3$

35.  $\dfrac{-12 + 4}{-5 - 3}$

36.  $\dfrac{3(-7) - (-5)^2}{2(-9) + (-28)}$

**Evaluate if x = 2,  y = -4,  and z = 6.**

37.  $-2z - 3y^2$

38.  $\dfrac{6x - 2y}{xy - 3z}$

39.  $(x - y)^2$

**Perform the indicated operations.**

40.  a.  $6a - 2a$    b.  $5x - 7y + 8x - 2y$

41.  a.  $4x^2 + 7 - x^2$    b.  $5w^2 - 9w - 3w^2 - 4w - 2$

42.  a.  $6xy + 4xy$    b.  $3x^3 - 2x^2 + 7x - 8x^3 + x^2 - 3x$

43.  a.  $4mn^2 - 3mn^2$    b.  $6a^2b^3 - 8a^2b^3$

44.  Subtract 2a from the sum of $5a + 6a$

45.  $6r^2s + 3mn - 2r^2s + mn$

46.  a.  $(2x^2y^2z^3)(5x^3y^2z^4)$    b.  $(-5x^2)(2x)$

47.  a.  $(7a^3)(4a^5)$    b.  $(3x^5yz^3)(2x^3y^2z)$

48.  a.  $\dfrac{24x^5}{6x^2}$    b.  $\dfrac{32x^5y^3}{4x^3y^2}$

49.  a.  $\dfrac{8m^3}{m^3}$    b.  $\dfrac{12a^3b^2c}{2a^2bc}$

50.  a.  $(3a^2b^2)(2a^2b^2)$    b.  $3a^2b^2 + 2a^2b^2$

Unit 1
Multiple Choice Review Form C

**Write the following phrase using symbols.**

1. 5 less than x

    a. 5 - x          c. x + 5

    b. x - 5          d. 5 + x

2. the product of 6 and a number decreased by 4

    a. 6 + x + 4        c. 6(x - 4)

    b. 6x - 4          d. $\dfrac{6}{x-4}$

**Use the Distributive Property to remove parentheses.**

3. 3(2x + 6y)

    a. 6x + 18y       c. 2x + 18y

    b. 6x + 6y        d. 6x - 18y

4. $2a(a^2 + 3b)$

    a. $2a^2 + 6ab$      c. $2a^3 + 6ab$

    b. $2a^3 + 3b$       d. $2a^2 + 6ab$

5. **Evaluate:** $3x^2y$ if x = 1 and y = 2.

    a. 12           c. 0

    b. 6            d. 7

6. **Evaluate:** 5 + (6 - 2) · 3

    a. 27           c. 12

    b. 17           d. 41

7. **Evaluate:** |-4|
    a. 4         c. 1

    b. -4        d. 0

8. **Evaluate:** - |-6|
    a. 6         c. -6

    b. 0         d. 1

**Evaluate.**

9.  -8 + 12
    a. -4      c. 20
    b. 96      d. 4

10.  -5 - 10
    a. 15      c. -5
    b. 5      d. -15

11.  (-3) - (-1) - 2 + 4
    a. -2      c. 2
    b. 0      d. -10

12.  (-2)(-3)
    a. -6      c. 5
    b. 6      d. -5

13.  (-6)(4)
    a. -24      c. 24
    b. -10      d. 10

14.  (-3) - (-2)(4)
    a. 2      c. 5
    b. -1      d. -3

15.  $\dfrac{-35}{-7}$
    a. 1      c. -5
    b. 6      d. 5

16.  $\dfrac{-24}{6}$
    a. -4      c. 6
    b. 4      d. 12

17.  $\dfrac{9}{0}$
    a. 0      c. 9
    b. undefined      d. -9

18.  $\dfrac{0}{-3}$
    a. undefined      c. 0
    b. -3      d. 3

19. $4 - 3(5 - 6)^3$
   - a. 13
   - c. 1
   - b. -1
   - d. 7

20. **Evaluate** $\dfrac{2xy - y^2}{2x - 3y}$ **if** $x = 3$ **and** $y = -2$.
   - a. $\dfrac{-8}{3}$
   - c. undefined
   - b. $\dfrac{-4}{3}$
   - d. $\dfrac{8}{3}$

21. **Evaluate** $a^2 - 2bc$ **if** $a = 2,\ b = -1$ **and** $c = 4$.
   - a. -8
   - c. 12
   - b. 24
   - d. 8

**Perform the indicated operations.**

22. $4x^2y + 3ab - 2x^2y - ab$
   - a. $2x^2y + 2ab$
   - c. $2x^2y + 4ab$
   - b. $2x^2y + 3ab$
   - d. $6x^2y + 2ab$

23. $(2x^2y^3)(3xy^5)$
   - a. $6x^2y^8$
   - c. $6x^3y^8$
   - b. $5x^3y^{15}$
   - d. $6x^2y^{15}$

24. $\dfrac{18a^4b^{12}}{9a^2b^4}$
   - a. $2a^2b^8$
   - c. $2a^2b^3$
   - b. $9a^2b$
   - d. $2a^6b^{16}$

25. **Evaluate** $2x^2 - y^2 + 4z^3$ **if** $x = 4,\ y = 3$ **and** $z = 2$.
   - a. 58
   - c. 39
   - b. 248
   - d. 55

**Answers to Unit 1,  Review Form A**

| | | | | | |
|---|---|---|---|---|---|
| 1a.  c - 4 | 1b.  x - 7 | 2a.  b + 4 | 2b.  $2(3-x)$ | 3a.  8 - x | 3b.  5x + y |

4a.  $5(x+y)$   4b.  $\dfrac{6-y}{7-y}$   5a.  xyz   5b.  $3(x+2)$   6a.  7/x   6b.  6/y

7.  $15a + 20b$   8.  $2ab + ac$   9.  $3xy + 12x$   10.  $3^2b^5$   11.  $7^3h^4$   12a.  3

12b.  53   12c.  1   12d.  14   13a.  18   13b.  36   13c.  36

14a.  11   14b.  5/8   14c.  39   15a.  $-5$   15b.  3   15c.  $-1$

16a.  10   16b.  7   16c.  -6   16d.  $-2$   7a.  0   17b.  $-1$

17c.  0   17d.  $-10$   18a.  -10   18b.  -12   18c.  -25   18d.  -10

19a.  10   19b.  26   19c.  $-13$   19d.  $-37$   20a.  -6   20b.   0

20c.  9   20d.  10   21a.  -5   21b.   6   21c.  9   21d.  7

22.  3/14   23.  $-10\dfrac{1}{3}$   24.  1.15   25.  0   26a.  $-15$   26b.  $-16$

26c.  24   27a.  $-9$   27b.  16   27c.  $-1$   28a.  3   28b.  $-6$

28c.  $-3$   29a.  0   29b. undefined 29c.  $-1$   30a.  $-6$   30b.  5

31a.  45   31b.  $-10$   32a.  1   32b.  17   33a.  -20   33b.  16

34.  7   35.  4   36.  $-\dfrac{1}{2}$   37.  $-13$   38.  $-\dfrac{8}{9}$   39.  25

40a.  4x   40b.  $-5x - 8y$   41a.  $a^2 + 5$   41b.  $3a^2 - 2b^2 + 5$   42a.  7ab

42b.  $-3x^3 - 6x^2 - 3x$   43a.  $7m^2n$   43b.  $11a^2b^2$   44.  $9x^2$   45.  $ab + 7xy$

46a.  $6a^3b^4c^6$   46b.  $-12x^3$   47a.  $20x^6$   47b.  $14x^5y^6z^3$ 48a.  $5a^2$   48b.  $3x^2y$

49a.  15   49b.  6xz   50a.  $15x^4y^6$   50b.  $8x^2y^3$

## Answers to Unit 1, Review Form B

1a. $ab$  1b. $\dfrac{x}{x+y}$  2a. $x - 8$  2b. $5 - x$  3a. $a + 6$  3b. $3(c - d)$

4a. $7(x + y)$  4b. $7x + y$  5a. $4abc$  5b. $2(r + s)$  6. $\dfrac{x+3}{3-x}$

7. $4x + 6y$  8. $rs + 2rt$  9. $6a + 3ab$  10. $4^3 k^5$  11. $7^2 d^3 e f^2$  12a. $2$

12b. $38$  12c. $29$  12d. $12$  13a. $36$  13b. $144$  13c. $27$

14a. $11$  14b. $\dfrac{1}{3}$  14c. $18$  15a. $2$  15b. $-6$  15c. $-4$

16a. $9$  16b. $7$  16c. $1$  16d. $-10$  17a. $0$  17b. $-24$

17c. $-2$  17d. $4$  18a. $-15$  18b. $-38$  18c. $-7$  18d. $-10$

19a. $7$  19b. $11$  19c. $-6$  19d. $10$  20a. $-8$  20b. $-4$

20c. $13$  20d. $8$  21a. $6$  21b. $10$  21c. $14$  21d. $5$

22. $\dfrac{1}{8}$  23. $-6\dfrac{1}{3}$  24. $.08$  25. $0$  26a. $-40$  26b. $-24$

26c. $36$  27a. $-4$  27b. $4$  27c. $-1$  28a. $-6$  28b. $4$

28c. $9$  29a. undefined  29b. $0$  29c. $-1$  30a. $-5$  30b. $-4$

31a. $18$  31b. $12$  32a. $8$  32b. $20$  33a. $-16$  33b. $20$

34. $8$  35. $1$  36. $1$  37. $-60$  38. $-\dfrac{10}{13}$  39. $36$

40a. $4a$  40b. $3x - 9y$  41a. $3x^2 + 7$  41b. $2w^2 - 13w - 24$  42a. $10xy$

42b. $-5x^3 - x^2 + 4x$  43a. $mn^2$  43b. $-2a^2 b^3$  44. $9a^2$

45. $4mn + 4r^2 s$  46a. $10x^5 y^4 z^7$  46b. $-10x^3$  47a. $28a^8$  47b. $6x^8 y^3 z^4$

48a. $4x^3$  48b. $8x^2 y$  49a. $8$  49b. $6ab$  50a. $6a^4 b^4$

50b. $5a^2 b^2$

## Answers to Unit 1, Multiple Choice Review Form C

1. b  2. c  3. a  4. c  5. b
6. b  7. a  8. c  9. d  10. d
11. b  12. b  13. a  14. c  15. d
16. a  17. b  18. c  19. d  20. b
21. c  22. a  23. c  24. a  25. d

# Elementary Algebra Review

# Unit 2

# Equations and Inequalities

**Solve the following equations and check your answers.**

1. $x - 5 = 9$

2. $3b = 2b - 5$

3. $5x = -10$

4. $3y - 2 = 5$

5. $6 - 4x = -x$

6. $7 - 2r = 3r + 2$

7. $6x - 5 = 8x + 10 + x$

8. $3(z - 2) = -2 + 5z + 9$

9. $\dfrac{3x}{4} = -24$

10. $\dfrac{5}{8}a + 2 = 8 - \dfrac{3}{8}a$

11. $x - 2(x - 3) = 4x + 1$

12. $4(x - 3) = 2 - (x - 5)$

13. $6 - 3(2x + 1) = 4x + 3(x - 2) - 4$

**Solve the following literal equations for the indicated variable.**

14. $I = PRT$  (for R)

15. $y = mx + b$  (for x)

16. $P = 2L + 2W$  (for L)

17. $D = \dfrac{C - s}{n}$  (for C)

18. $-3x + 4y = -5$  (for y)

**Solve and graph the solution for each of the inequalities.**

19. $x - 5 > 2$

20. $5 - x < 7$

21. $3x - 5 \geq 5x + 2$

22. $\dfrac{2x}{5} < 10$

23. $-5x + 1 \leq -3(x - 3) + 2$

**Solve the following applications.**

24. The difference between twice a number and 6 is 22.  Find the number.

25. The sum of two consecutive odd integers is 68.  Find the integers.

$$x, \quad x + 2, \quad x + 4$$
$$x + x + 2 = 68$$
$$2x + 2 = 68$$
$$2x = 66$$
$$x = 33, 35$$

17

26. Four times an integer is 30 less than five times the next consecutive even integer. Find the integers.

27. Mrs. Shimp is 10 years less than twice as old as her daughter. If the difference between their ages is 18, how old is Mrs. Shimp? How old is her daughter?

28. The length of a rectangle is 4 inches more than twice its width. If the perimeter is 44 inches, what are the dimensions of the rectangle?

29. One positive integer is 3 more than twice another. If three times the smaller integer is one less than the larger, what are the two integers?

30. Tickets for the honor society banquet are $6 for students and $10 for guests. Total receipts for the banquet were $3,040. If there were 120 more guest tickets than student tickets, how many students attended the banquet?

31. Janelle has twice as many quarters as dimes. If the total value is $2.40, how many of each type coin does she have?

32. David rode his motorbike to Grandmom's house in 2 hours. His return trip took 3 hours and his speed was 10 mph less then when going. What was his rate going to Grandmom's house?

**Solve the following equations and check your answers.**

1.  $x - 4 = 11$

2.  $5a = 4a - 3$

3.  $6y = -7$

4.  $4x - 3 = 9$

5.  $8 - 5x = -x$

6.  $6 - 5x = 2x - 1$

7.  $7x - 3 = 3x + 11 - x$

8.  $3(a - 5) = -5 + 7a + 2$

9.  $\dfrac{2x}{3} = -24$

10.  $\dfrac{7}{8}y - 2 = 10 - \dfrac{1}{8}y$

11.  $x - 3(x - 2) = 5x - 1$

12.  $5(x - 2) = 1 - (x + 5)$

13.  $8 - 4(2x + 1) = 2x + 3(x - 3) - 6$

**Solve the following literal equations for the indicated variable.**

14. $I = PRT$   (for P)

15. $y = mx + b$   (for b)

16. $P = 2L + 2W$   (for W)

17. $D = \dfrac{C - s}{n}$   (for n)

18. $-5x + 2y = -3$   (for y)

**Solve and graph the solution set for each of the inequalities.**

19. $x - 6 > -1$

20. $4 - x \geq 3$

21. $5x - 1 \geq 3x + 3$

22. $\dfrac{2x}{3} < 6$

23. $-2x + 7 < -5(x - 1) + 3$

**Solve the following applications.**

24. The difference between twice a number and 4 is 10. Find the number.

25. The sum of two consecutive even integers is 38. Find the integers.

$x,\ x+2$

$x + x + 2 = 38$

$2x + 2 = 38$

$\dfrac{2x = 36}{2}$

$x = 18,\ 20$

26. Three times an integer is 27 less than four times the next consecutive integer. Find the integers.

27. A washer and dryer are on sale as a combination deal for $570. If the dryer is $80 less than the washer, how much does each appliance cost?

28. The length of a rectangle is 6 inches more than three times its width. If the perimeter is 84 inches, what are the dimensions of the rectangle?

29. One integer is 5 more than another. If three times the smaller integer is one less than the twice the larger, what are the two integers?

30. Tickets for Jurassic Park are $6.00 for adults and $4.50 for children. Your total bill was $40.50. If there were 2 more children tickets than adult tickets, how many of each type of ticket did you buy?

31. Heather has 3 more nickels than dimes, and twice as many quarters as dimes in her purse. If the total value is $3.40, how many of each type coin does she have?

32. The length of a rectangle is 2 inches more than four times its width. If the perimeter is 44 inches, find the dimensions of the rectangle.

**Solve the following equations and check your answers.**

1. $-5x = -x + 8$

    a. $x = -2$      b. $x = 2$

    c. $x = \dfrac{-4}{3}$      d. $x = \dfrac{4}{3}$

2. $7y - 4 = 3y + 8$

    a. $y = 1$      b. $y = 3$

    c. $y = 4$      d. $y = \dfrac{6}{5}$

3. $2(a - 3) = -5 + 8a + 2$

    a. $a = \dfrac{-1}{2}$      b. $a = \dfrac{1}{2}$

    c. $a = 0$      d. $a = \dfrac{1}{10}$

4. $2x + 5(x - 2) = 5 - (x - 1)$

    a. $x = 2$      b. $x = -2$

    c. $x = \dfrac{1}{2}$      d. $x = \dfrac{2}{3}$

5. $x - 3(x - 2) = 5x - (x + 3)$

    a. $x = \dfrac{-1}{2}$      b. $x = \dfrac{-3}{2}$

    c. $x = \dfrac{3}{2}$      d. $x = 2$

**Solve the following literal equations for the indicated variable.**

6. $V = lwh$    (for w)

    a. $w = V - lh$      b. $w = \dfrac{V}{lh}$

    c. $w = (V - l)h$      d. $w = \dfrac{lh}{V}$

7. $S = \dfrac{1}{2}gt^2$

    a. $g = \dfrac{t^2}{S}$      b. $g = \dfrac{2S}{t^2}$

    c. $g = 2St^2$      d. $g = \dfrac{St^2}{2}$

8.　$-6x + 2y = -5$　(for y)

a.　$y = 6x - 5$　　b.　$y = -3x + \dfrac{5}{2}$　　c.　$y = 3x - \dfrac{5}{2}$　　d.　$y = -6x - \dfrac{5}{2}$

**Solve and graph the solution set for each of the inequalities.**

9.　$6 - x \leq 2$

    a.　$x \leq 4$

    b.　$x \geq -4$

    c.　$x \geq 4$

    d.　$x \leq -4$

10.　$-2x + 5 < -4(x - 1) + 3$

    a.　$x < 1$

    b.　$-1 < x$

    c.　$x > 1$

    d.　$x < -1$

**Solve the following applications.**

11.　The difference between three times a number and 4 is 11.　　　Find the number.

    a.　$x = 5$　　b.　$x = 4$　　c.　$x = \dfrac{7}{3}$　　d.　$x = \dfrac{14}{3}$

12.　The length of a rectangle is 2 inches more than three times its width.  If the perimeter is 28 inches, what are the dimensions of the rectangle?

    a.　8 in. by 20 in.　　b. 12 in. by 16 in.　　c.  3 in. by 11 in.　　d.  none of the above

13.　The length of a rectangle is 5 more than its width.  How would you represent the perimeter of the rectangle if the width is represented by w?

    a.  $P = (w - 5) + w$　　b.  $P = 2(w - 5) + 2w$　　c.  $P = 2(w + 5) + 2w$　　d.  $P = 2L + 2W$

## Answers to Unit 2, Review Form A

1. $x = 14$
2. $b = -5$
3. $x = -2$
4. $y = 7/3$
5. $x = 2$
6. $r = 1$
7. $x = -5$
8. $z = -13/2$
9. $x = -32$
10. $a = 6$
11. $x = 1$
12. $x = 19/5$
13. $x = 1$
14. $I/PT = R$
15. $(y - b)/m = x$
16. $(P-2W)/2 = L$
17. $Dn + s = C$
18. $(3x - 5)/4 = y$
19. $x > 7$
20. $x > -2$
21. $x \le -7/2$
22. $x < 25$
23. $x \ge -5$
24. $x = 14$
25. 33, 35
26. 20, 22
27. 46, 28
28. Width 6 in., Length 16 in.
29. 2 and 7
30. 115 students
31. 4 dimes, 8 quarters
32. 30 mph

## Answers to Unit 2, Review Form B

1. $x = 15$
2. $a = -3$
3. $y = -7/6$
4. $x = 3$
5. $x = 2$
6. $x = 1$
7. $x = 14/5$
8. $a = -3$
9. $x = -36$
10. $y = 12$
11. $x = 1$
12. $x = 1$
13. $x = 19/13$
14. $I/RT = P$
15. $y - mx = b$
16. $(P - 2L)/2 = W$
17. $n = (c - s)/D$
18. $y = (5x - 3)/2$
19. $x > 5$
20. $x \le 1$
21. $x \ge 2$
22. $x < 9$
23. $x < 1/3$
24. $x = 7$
25. 18, 20
26. 23, 24
27. Dryer $245, Washer $325
28. Width 9 in., Length 33 in.
29. 9, 14
30. 5 Children
    3 Adult
31. 8 Nickels
    5 Dimes
    10 Quarters
32. Width 4 in.
    Length 18 in.

## Answers to Unit 2, Multiple Choice Review Form C

| 1. a | 2. b | 3. a | 4. a | 5. c |
|------|------|------|------|------|
| 6. b | 7. b | 8. c | 9. c | 10. a |
| 11. a | 12. c | 13. c | | |

# Elementary Algebra Review

# Unit 3

# Polynomials

**Multiply.**

1. a) $x^2y^3 \bullet x^4y^5$     b) $-3a^3b^5 \bullet 4a^2b^3 \bullet b$

**Divide.**

2. a) $\dfrac{-24x^6y^8}{3x^4y^5}$     b) $\dfrac{6a^4b^2 \bullet 4a^5b^4}{2a^3b^5}$

**Simplify.**

3. a) $(p^3)^5$     b) $(3x^3y^2)^4$

   c) $\dfrac{\left(x^2\right)^3\left(x^4\right)^4}{\left(x^3\right)^2}$     d) $3 \bullet 3^2 \bullet 3^5$

**Evaluate.**

4. a) $8^0$     b) $-5m^0$     c) $\left(2x^2y^4\right)^0$

**Simplify. Write your answers with only positive exponents.**

5. a) $y^{-4}$     b) $2^{-3}$     c) $5a^{-7}$

6. a) $x^5 \bullet x^{-3}$     b) $y^{-4} \bullet y^2$     c) $z^{-5} \bullet z^0$

7. a) $\dfrac{a^3}{a^{-5}}$     b) $\dfrac{m^{-5}}{m^{-10}}$     c) $\dfrac{\left(x^{-2}\right)^3}{\left(x^4\right)^{-2}}$

**Express each number in scientific notation.**

8. a) 450,000,000     b) 0.00000000236     c) 0.000000251

**Write each expression in standard form.**

9. a) $2.15 \times 10^{-5}$     b) $3.7 \times 10^6$     c) $3.8 \times 10^4$

**Classify the following polynomials and state the degree.**

10. $6x - 2$

11. $5x^4 - 7x^2 + 3$

**Find the value for the following expressions if x = - 2 and y = 3.**

12. a) $3x^2 + 7x + 3$

b) $3x^3 - 2y$

13. **Simplify.** $5m - (3m - 4p)$

**Perform the indicated operations.**

14. Add. $6x^2 - 5x$ and $4x^2 + 3x$

15. Add. $3x^5 - 2x + 3x^3$ and $6x - 4x^5 + 7x^3$

16. a) Subtract x from 6

b) Subtract x - 4 from 3x - 5

17. Subtract $3x^2 - 2x + 5$ from $6x^2 + 7x - 2$

**Multiply the following.**

18. a) $(3x^2)(-4x^5)$

b) $3r^2s (2r^3s^2 - 5r^2s + rs^2)$

19. a) $(x + 6)(3x + 2)$

b) $(x - 4y)(x + 4y)$

20. a) $(3x - 5)(4x + 3)$

b) $(2a - 5)^2$

21. a) $2x(x - 3)(2x + 5)$

b) $(2a + 3)(3a^2 - 2a + 1)$

**Divide the following.**

22. a) $\dfrac{6x^5y^2 + 4x^6y}{2x^3y}$

b) $\dfrac{24a^5b^3 - 12a^4b^2 + 8a^2b}{4a^2b}$

**Optional:**

23. $x - 4 \overline{\smash{\big)}\,x^2 - 13x + 36}$

24. $(4x^2 - 6x + 3) \div (2x + 1)$

25. $(6x^3 + 13x^2 + 10x + 8) \div (2x + 3)$

30

**Multiply.**

1. a) $m^3n^2 \bullet m^4n^5$ 

       b) $-5a^2b^3 \bullet 2a^5b^7 \bullet b$

**Divide.**

2. a) $\dfrac{-35x^7y^2}{5x^4y^5}$ 

       b) $\dfrac{3r^2s^4 \bullet 9r^5s^2}{3r^3s}$

**Simplify.**

3. a) $(m^4)^6$ 

       b) $(2x^5y^3)^4$

   c) $\dfrac{(x^3)^5 \, (x^2)^3}{\left(x^6\right)^3}$ 

       d) $2 \bullet 2^3 \bullet 2^7$

**Evaluate.**

4. a) $3^0$        b) $-2a^0$        c) $(3m^4n^2)^0$

**Simplify. Write your answers with only positive exponents.**

5. a) $y^{-6}$        b) $2^{-4}$        c) $7a^{-5}$

6. a) $x^4 \bullet x^{-6}$        b) $y^{-2} \bullet y^7$        c) $z^{-3} \bullet z^0$

7. a) $\dfrac{s^3}{s^{-2}}$        b) $\dfrac{m^{-5}}{m^{-3}}$        c) $\dfrac{(x^{-3})^2}{\left(x^5\right)^{-3}}$

**Express each number in scientific notation.**

8. a) 56,000,000        b) 0.00000042        c) 3,250,000,000

**Write each expression in standard form.**

9. a) $3.8 \times 10^{-6}$        b) $4.12 \times 10^5$        c) $7.3 \times 10^{-4}$

**Classify the following polynomials and state the degree.**

10.  $4x^3 - 1$

11.  $2x^2 - 3x + 1$

**Find the value for the following expressions when $x = 2$ and $y = -3$**

12. a)  $-2y^2 + 3y - 4$

b)  $x^2y - 3y$

13. **Simplify.**  $a - (2b - 3a)$

**Perform the indicated operations.**

14.  Add  $4x^2 - 3x$  and  $-2x^2 + 5x$

15.  Add  $2x^4 - 3x + 4x^3$  and  $6x - 5x^4 - 7x^3$

16. a)  Subtract 7 from x

b)  Subtract $3x - 6$ from $2x + 8$

17.  Subtract  $-2x^2 + 4x - 6$  from  $3x^2 + 7x - 3$

**Multiply the following.**

18. a)  $(5a^2)(-3a^4)$

b)  $2x^3y(3x^4y^2 - x^2y + 6xy^3)$

19. a)  $(r - 2)(3r - 2)$

b)  $(x - 3y)(x + 3y)$

20. a)  $(2a - 3)(5a + 1)$

b)  $(2x - 3)^2$

21. a)  $3r(r - 2)(3r + 2)$

b)  $(2x - 3)(4x^2 - 3x + 2)$

**Divide the following.**

22.  a)  $\dfrac{8x^4y^5 - 6x^2y^6}{2x^2y^3}$

      b).  $\dfrac{18a^7b^2 - 12a^3b^4 + 6a^5b}{6a^3b}$

**Optional:**

23.  $x + 3 \overline{\smash{\big)}\,x^2 - 2x - 15}$

24.  $(6x^2 + 7x + 4) \div (3x + 2)$

25.  $(4x^3 + 4x^2 - 7x + 5) \div (2x - 1)$

**Simplify.**

1. $c^5 c^4$

    a. c      b. $c^{20}$      c. $c^9$      d. 9c

2. $(4x^3 y)(5xy^5)$

    a. $9x^3 y^5$      b. $20x^3 y^6$      c. $9x^4 y^6$      d. $20x^4 y^6$

3. $5a^0$

    a. 5      b. 5a      c. 1      d. 0

4. $\left( \dfrac{4b^2}{5c} \right)^2$

    a. $\dfrac{4b^4}{5c^2}$      b. $\dfrac{16b^4}{25c^2}$      c. $\dfrac{8b^4}{10c^2}$      d. $\dfrac{16b^2}{25c}$

**Write using positive Exponents.**

5. $5x^{-5}$

    a. $\dfrac{1}{5x^5}$      b. $\dfrac{x^5}{5}$      c. $\dfrac{5}{x^5}$      d. x

**Express the number in scientific notation:**

6.

    0.000000782

    a. $7.82 \times 10^7$      b. $7.82 \times 10^{-7}$

    c. $7.82 \times 10^{-6}$      d. $7.82 \times 10^6$

**Classify the following polynomial and state the degree.**

7. $5x^6 - 7x^4 + 2$

    a. binomial, 5th degree      b. monomial, 7th degree

    c. trinomial, 5th degree      d. trinomial, 6th degree

**Find the value for the following expression.**

8. $-3x^2 - 4x + 2$    when $x = -2$

    a. 22      b. -18      c. -2      d. 6

9. Subtract $-3x^2 + 2x - 3$ from $3x^2 + 5x - 7$

    a. 7x - 10      b. $6x^2 + 7x - 10$

    c. 3x - 4      d. $6x^2 + 3x - 4$

**Multiply the following.**

10.   $(2x - 5)(3x + 2)$

      a.  $5x^2 + 19x - 7$            b.  $6x^2 - 11x - 10$

      c.  $6x^2 + 11x - 10$          d.  $5x^2 - 4x - 7$

11.   $(2x - 3)^2$

      a.  $4x^2 - 9$               b.  $4x^2 - 12x + 9$

      c.  $4x^2 - 6x + 6$          d.  $4x^2 + 9$

**Divide the following.**

12.   $\dfrac{24a^5b^2 - 12a^6b^3 + 6a^3b}{6a^3b}$

      a.  $4a^2b^2 - 2a^2b^2 + 1$       b.  $4a^2b - 2a^3b^2$

      c.  $4a^2b - 2a^3b^2 + 1$      d.  $4a^2b - 6a^3b^2$

13.   $(8x^2 + 10x - 7) \div (4x - 1)$     **(Optional)**

      a.  $2x + 2 + \dfrac{-9}{4x-1}$       b.  $2x + 3 + \dfrac{-4}{4x-1}$

      c.  $2x - 3 + \dfrac{-10}{4x-1}$      d.  $2x - 2 + \dfrac{-5}{4x-1}$

**Unit 3**
Review Form D
Word Problem Practice

**Translate and solve.**

1.  The sum of two integers is 21. If x represents the larger integer, how would you represent the smaller integer?

2.  In a collection of coins there are twice as many quarters as nickels and two less dimes than nickels. If x represents the number of nickels, how would you represent the quarters and dimes?

3.  A twenty-four foot board is to be cut into two pieces. If x represents the longer piece, how would you represent the smaller piece?

4.  If you have x dimes and y quarters, how would you represent the total value of the coins?

5.  One number is two less than another. The sum of the numbers is twelve. What are the numbers?

6.  Three times a number is equal to eight more than the number. What is the number?

7.  The sum of two consecutive integers is twenty-one. What are the integers?

8.  The sum of three consecutive even integers is thirty-six. What are the integers?

9.  The cost of two printer cartridges is $65.00. If the color cartridge cost eleven dollars more than the black cartridge, how much does each type of cartridge costs?

10. Dorothy earns $420 more a month than Richard. Their total income for the month is $4,860. How much does each person make?

11. The width of a rectangle is six inches less than the length. If the perimeter is seventy-two inches, what are the dimensions of the rectangle?

12. The length of a rectangle is three more than twice the width. If the perimeter is forty-eight inches, what are the dimensions of the rectangle?

13. An equilateral triangle has three sides of equal length. If the perimeter of the triangle is twenty-four meters, how long is each side of the triangle?

14. The base of an isosceles triangle is four inches less than the length of the equal sides. If the perimeter of the triangle is twenty-six inches, how long is each side of the triangle?

15. One integer is two less than another. The larger integer plus four times the smaller equals thirty-seven. Find the integers.

$x, x-2$

$x + 4(x-2) = 37$
$x + 4x - 8 = 37$
$5x = 45$
$\boxed{x = 9}$

$y - 2 -$
$9 - 2 = 7$
$\boxed{x = 7}$

16. One positive integer is three more than twice another integer. The difference between four times the smaller integer and the larger integer is twenty-one. What are the numbers?

17. Janelle has lost thirty-six pounds in the past three months. If she lost eight more pounds the second month than she did in the first month, and two less pounds the third month than the first month, how many pounds has she lost each month?

18. Amber has $5.00 in her purse consisting of nickels, dimes, and quarters. If she has one more quarter than dimes, and one less nickel than dimes, how many of each type of coin does she have?

$5n + 10D + 25(d+1) = 500$  $5n + 100 + 25q = 500$  $q = d+1$  $q = 12+1$
$5(d-1) + 10D + 25(d+1) = 500$  $400 + 50 = 300$  $\boxed{q = 13}$
$5d - 5 + 10D + 25d + 25 = 500$  $\dfrac{400}{40} = \dfrac{480}{40}$  $\boxed{D = 12}$  $n = d-1$  $n = 12-1 = \boxed{n = 11}$

19. David won $118 in the lottery. The cashier paid him with one, five, and twenty-dollar bills. If he has twice as many one-dollar bills as twenty-dollar bills, and two more five-dollar bills than twenty-dollar bills, how many of each type of bill does he have?

20. Louis withdrew $150 from the ATM machine. The machine gave him nine bills made up of tens and twenties. How many of each kind of bill did he receive?

4 time as many as N as S
N = 4S

21. CCC's Little Theater earned $700 from the proceeds of its latest play. Student tickets were $5 and non-student tickets were $7.50. If there were four times as many non-students as students, how many of each type of ticket were sold?

$= 700$
$S = 5$
$NS = 7.50$
$5S + 7.5 NS = 700$
$N = 4S$
$N = 4(20)$
$\boxed{N = 80}$
$5S + 7.5(4s) = 700$
$5S + 30S = 700$
$35S = 700$
$\boxed{S = 20}$

22. Concert tickets are twenty dollars for the balcony and forty-five dollars for the mezzanine. If Jane bought eight tickets and spent $210, how many of each type of ticket did she buy?

23. Two planes leave Philadelphia at the same time. One plane heads east at two hundred mph and the other plane heads west at two hundred and thirty mph. How long will it take for them to be 1,290 miles apart?

24. A train leaves City A heading for City B at 11 a.m. traveling 75 mph. An hour later, a second train leaves City B heading for City A traveling 80 mph. At what time will the trains pass each other if the cities are 385 miles apart?

25. It took David two hours to ride his bike to camp and one hour to ride home. His rate going home was 10 mph faster than going to camp. How fast did he travel each way?

**Answers to Unit 3, Review Form A**

1. a) $x^6y^8$      b) $-12a^5b^9$

2. a) $-8x^2y^3$      b) $12a^6b$

3. a) $p^{15}$      b) $81x^{12}y^8$
   c) $x^{20}$      d) $3^8$

4. a) $1$    b) $-5$    c) $1$

5. a) $\dfrac{1}{y^4}$    b) $\dfrac{1}{8}$    c) $\dfrac{5}{a^7}$

6. a) $x^2$    b) $\dfrac{1}{y^2}$    c) $\dfrac{1}{z^5}$

7. a) $a^8$    b) $m^5$    c) $x^2$

8. a) $4.5\times10^8$ b) $2.36\times10^{-9}$ c) $2.51\times10^{-7}$

9. a) $0.0000215$ b) $3,700,000$ c) $38,000$

10. Binomial, 1st degree

11. Trinomial, 4th degree

12. a) $1$     b) $-30$

13. $2m + 4p$

14. $10x^2 - 2x$

15. $-x^5 + 10x^3 + 4x$

16. a) $6 - x$      b) $2x - 1$

17. $3x^2 + 9x - 7$

18. a) $-12x^7$   b) $6r^5s^3 - 15r^4s^2 + 3r^3s^3$

19. a) $3x^2 + 20x + 12$    b) $x^2 - 16y^2$

20. a) $12x^2 - 11x - 15$
   b) $4a^2 - 20a + 25$

21. a) $4x^3 - 2x^2 - 30x$
   b) $6a^3 + 5a^2 - 4a + 3$

22. a) $3x^2y + 2x^3$
   b) $6a^3b^2 - 3a^2b + 2$

23. $x - 9$

24. $2x - 4 + \dfrac{7}{2x+1}$

25. $3x^2 + 2x + 2 + \dfrac{2}{2x+3}$

**Answers to Unit 3, Review Form B**

1. a) $m^7n^7$      b) $-10a^7b^{11}$

2. a) $\dfrac{-7x^3}{y^3}$      b) $9r^4s^5$

3. a) $m^{24}$      b) $16x^{20}y^{12}$
   c) $x^3$      d) $2^{11}$

4. a) $1$    b) $-2$    c) $1$

5. a) $\dfrac{1}{y^6}$    b) $\dfrac{1}{16}$    c) $\dfrac{7}{a^5}$

6. a) $\dfrac{1}{x^2}$    b) $y^5$    c) $\dfrac{1}{z^3}$

7. a) $s^5$    b) $\dfrac{1}{m^2}$    c) $x^9$

8. a) $5.6\times10^7$ b) $4.2\times10^{-7}$ c) $3.25\times10^9$

9. a) $0.0000038$    b) $412,000$    c) $0.00073$

10. Binomial, 3rd degree

11. Trinomial, 2nd degree

12. a) $-31$     b) $-3$

13. $4a - 2b$

14. $2x^2 + 2x$

15. $-3x^4 - 3x^3 + 3x$

16. a) $x - 7$      b) $-x + 14$

17. $5x^2 + 3x + 3$

18. a) $-15a^6$    b) $6x^7y^3 - 2x^5y^2 + 12x^4y^4$

19. a) $3r^2 - 8r + 4$    b) $x^2 - 9y^2$

20. a) $10a^2 - 13a - 3$
   b) $4x^2 - 12x + 9$

21. a) $9r^3 - 12r^2 - 12r$
   b) $8x^3 - 18x^2 + 13x - 6$

22. a) $4x^2y^2 - 3y^3$
   b) $3a^4b - 2b^3 + a^2$

23. $x - 5$

24. $2x + 1 + \dfrac{2}{3x+2}$

25. $2x^2 + 3x - 2 + \dfrac{3}{2x-1}$

## Answers to Unit 3, Multiple Choice Review Form C

| 1. c | 2. d | 3. a | 4. b | 5. c | 6. b | 7. d |
|------|------|------|------|------|------|------|
| 8. c | 9. d | 10. b | 11. b | 12. c | 13. b | |

## Answers to Unit 3, Review Form D - Word Problem Review

1.  $21 - x$

2.  $2x$ = Quarters,  $x - 2$ = Dimes

3.  $24 - x$

4.  $.10x + .25y$

5.  5, 7

6.  4

7.  10, 11

8.  10, 12, 14

9.  $27, $38

10.  Richard $2,220  Dorothy $2,640

11.  Length 21 in., Width 15 in.

12.  Length 17 in., Width 7 in.

13.  All sides are 8 meters

14.  Base is 6 in., equal sides are 10 in.

15.  7, 9

16.  12, 27

17.  10, 18, 8

18.  11 nickels, 12 dimes, 13 quarters

19.  8 $1,  6 $5,  4 $20

20.  3 $10,  6 $20

21.  20 student , 80 non-student

22.  2 mezzanine, 6 balcony

23.  3 hours

24.  2 p.m.

25.  10 mph,  20 mph

# Elementary Algebra Review

# Unit 4

# Factoring

Unit 4
Review Form A

**Factor**

1. $3x^5 + 9x^3$

2. $5x^4y^5 - 15x^2y^7$

3. $20x^2 + 5x$

4. $5(a + b) + c(a + b)$

5. $64x^2 - y^2$

6. $9x^2 - 49y^2$

7. $25x^2y^2 - 1$

8. $16x^4 - 81y^2$

9. $x^2 - 7xy - 8y^2$

10. $x^2 + 8x + 15$

11. $x^2 - 10x + 24$

12. $x^2 + 9xy - 22y^2$

13. $2x^2 - 17x + 15$

14. $12x^2 - 8x - 15$

15. $9x^2 - 6x + 1$

16. $4x^2 + 12x - 7$

17. $16x^2 - 4$

18. $5x^2 - 5x - 60$

19. $81x^4 + 9x^2$

20. $9x^2 + 3x - 6$

21. $7x^5 - 28x^3$

22. $x^3 - 5x^2 - 6x$

**23-24 Optional topic: factor by grouping**

23. $ax + cx + ay + cy$

24. $x^3 + 3x^2 + 2x + 6$

**Find the solution set**

25. $(x - 3)(2x + 5) = 0$

26. $x^2 - 81 = 0$

27. $x^2 - 8x = -12$

28. $3x^2 - 20x - 7 = 0$

29. The product of a number and 5 less than the same number is 24. Find the two numbers.

30. The area of a rectangle is 63 in$^2$. If the width is 2 inches shorter than the length, what are the dimensions of the rectangle?

Unit 4
Review Form B

**Factor**

1. $2x^3 + 6x^2$

2. $7x^3y^2 - 21x^5y$

3. $12x^2 + 4x$

4. $3(x + y) + z(x + y)$

5. $49x^2 - y^2$

6. $25x^2 - 9y^2$

7. $64x^2y^2 - 1$

8. $9x^4 - 4y^2$

9. $x^2 - 5xy + 4y^2$

10. $x^2 + 7x + 12$

11. $x^2 - 10x - 24$

12. $x^2 + 7xy - 30y^2$

13. $3x^2 - 13x - 10$

14. $15x^2 - 14x + 3$

15. $6x^2 - x - 15$

16. $4x^2 + 11x + 7$

17. $9x^2 - 81$                    18. $3x^2 - 3x - 6$

19. $16x^4 + 64x^2$              20. $8x^2 + 8x + 2$

21. $3x^3 - 12x$                    22. $x^3 - 5x^2 + 6x$

**23-24 Optional topic: factor by grouping**

23. $ax + 3x + 3a + 9$        24. $x^3 + 4x^2 + 3x + 12$

**Find the solution set**

25. $(x + 5)(5x - 3) = 0$      26. $x^2 - 64 = 0$

27. $x^2 - 9x = -20$             28. $2x^2 - 7x - 15 = 0$

29. The product of a number and 3 less than the same number is 10. Find the two numbers.

30. The area of a rectangle is 80 cm². If the length is 2 cm more than the width, what are the dimensions of the rectangle?

## Unit 4
## Multiple Choice Review Form C

### Factor

1. $x^2 - 6x - 16$

   A. $(x - 8)(x - 2)$
   B. $(x + 8)(x - 2)$
   C. $(x - 8)(x + 2)$
   D. $(x - 10)(x - 6)$

2. $x^2 - 10x + 25$

   A. $(x - 5)(x - 5)$
   B. $(x - 5)(x + 5)$
   C. $(x + 5)(x + 5)$
   D. $(x - 8)(x - 2)$

3. $2x^2 - 11x + 5$

   A. $(2x - 5)(x + 1)$
   B. $(2x + 1)(x - 6)$
   C. $(2x - 1)(x + 6)$
   D. $(2x - 1)(x - 5)$

4. $3x^2 - 2x - 5$

   A. $(3x - 5)(x + 1)$
   B. $(2x + 3)(x + 2)$
   C. $(3x - 5)(x - 1)$
   D. $(3x + 1)(x - 5)$

### Find one factor of the following expressions

5. $x^4 - 25$

   A. $x - 5$
   B. $x - 25$
   C. $x^2 - 25$
   D. $x^2 - 5$

6. $x^3 - 4x$

   A. $x^2 - x$
   B. $x$
   C. $x - 4$
   D. $x^2 - 2$

7. $7x^2 + 2x - 5$

   A. $7x - 5$
   B. $7x + 5$
   C. $7x - 1$
   D. $7x + 1$

8. $6x^2 - 11x - 10$

   A. $2x + 5$
   B. $3x + 2$
   C. $3x + 5$
   D. $3x - 2$

### Find the solution set

9. $15x^2 - 4x = 4$

   A. $\left\{\dfrac{2}{3}, -\dfrac{2}{5}\right\}$
   B. $\left\{-\dfrac{2}{3}, \dfrac{2}{5}\right\}$

   C. $\left\{-\dfrac{3}{2}, \dfrac{5}{2}\right\}$
   D. $\{2, -2\}$

10. $x^3 - 9x = 0$

   A. $\{0, 9\}$

   B. $\{0, 3\}$

   C. $\{3, -3\}$

   D. $\{0, 3, -3\}$

**Factor Completely**

1.  $x^2 - 9$

2.  $x^2 - 9x + 8$

3.  $9x^2 - 81$

4.  $3x^2 + 15x + 18$

5.  $x^2 - 10x - 24$

6.  $x^2 + 16$

7.  $3x^5y^3 - 12x^4y^5$

8.  $3(x - 2) + y(x - 2)$

9.  $6x^3 - 24x$

10.  $3x^2 + 19x + 6$

11.  $9x - 18$

12.  $4x^2 - 81$

13.  $3x^2 + 7xy + 4y^2$

14.  $4x^2 + 8x + 12$

15.  $x^2 - 10x + 24$

16.  $49x^2 - 25y^2$

17.  $x^2 + 7x - 9$

18.  $6x^2 - 11x - 10$

19.  $x^2 - xy - 12y^2$

20.  $4x^2 + 64$

21.  $5x^3y + 10x^5y^2 + 15x^7y^3$

## Answers to Unit 4, Review Form A

1. $3x^3(x^2 + 3)$
2. $5x^2y^5(x^2 - 3y^2)$
3. $5x(4x + 1)$
4. $(a + b)(5 + c)$

5. $(8x - y)(8x + y)$
6. $(3x - 7y)(3x + 7y)$
7. $(5xy - 1)(5xy + 1)$
8. $(4x^2 - 9y)(4x^2 + 9y)$

9. $(x - 8y)(x + y)$
10. $(x + 3)(x + 5)$
11. $(x - 6)(x - 4)$
12. $(x + 11y)(x - 2y)$

13. $(2x - 15)(x - 1)$
14. $(6x + 5)(2x - 3)$
15. $(3x - 1)(3x - 1)$
16. $(2x + 7)(2x - 1)$

17. $4(2x - 1)(2x + 1)$
18. $5(x - 4)(x + 3)$
19. $9x^2(9x^2 + 1)$
20. $3(3x - 2)(x + 1)$

21. $7x^3(x - 2)(x + 2)$
22. $x(x - 6)(x + 1)$
23. $(a + c)(x + y)$
24. $(x^2 + 2)(x + 3)$

25. $\left\{3, -\dfrac{5}{2}\right\}$
26. $\{9, -9\}$
27. $\{2, 6\}$
28. $\left\{7, -\dfrac{1}{3}\right\}$

29. 8,3 or -3, -8
30. 7 in, 9 in

## Answers to Unit 4, Review Form B

1. $2x^2(x + 3)$
2. $7x^3y(y - 3x^2)$
3. $4x(3x + 1)$
4. $(x + y)(3 + z)$

5. $(7x - y)(7x + y)$
6. $(5x - 3y)(5x + 3y)$
7. $(8xy - 1)(8xy + 1)$
8. $(3x^2 - 2y)(3x^2 + 2y)$

9. $(x - 4y)(x - y)$
10. $(x + 3)(x + 4)$
11. $(x - 12)(x + 2)$
12. $(x + 10y)(x - 3y)$

13. $(3x + 2)(x - 5)$
14. $(5x - 3)(3x - 1)$
15. $(3x - 5)(2x + 3)$
16. $(4x + 7)(x + 1)$

17. $9(x - 3)(x + 3)$
18. $3(x - 2)(x + 1)$
19. $16x^2(x^2 + 4)$
20. $2(2x + 1)(2x + 1)$

21. $3x(x - 2)(x + 2)$
22. $x(x - 3)(x - 2)$
23. $(x + 3)(a + 3)$
24. $(x^2 + 3)(x + 4)$

25. $\left\{-5, \dfrac{3}{5}\right\}$
26. $\{8, -8\}$
27. $\{5, 4\}$
28. $\left\{5, -\dfrac{3}{2}\right\}$

29. 5, 2 or -2, -5
30. 8 cm, 10 cm

## Answers to Unit 4, Multiple Choice Review Form C

1. C    2. A    3. D    4. A    5. D    6. B    7. A    8. B    9. A    10. D

## Answers to Unit 4, Review Form D

1. $(x - 3)(x + 3)$
2. $(x - 8)(x - 1)$
3. $9(x - 3)(x + 3)$
4. $3(x + 2)(x + 3)$

5. $(x - 12)(x + 2)$
6. Prime
7. $3x^4y^3(x - 4y^2)$
8. $(3 + y)(x - 2)$

9. $6x(x - 2)(x + 2)$
10. $(3x + 1)(x + 6)$
11. $9(x - 2)$
12. $(2x - 9)(2x + 9)$

13. $(3x + 4y)(x + y)$
14. $4(x^2 + 2x + 3)$
15. $(x - 6)(x - 4)$
16. $(7x - 5y)(7x + 5y)$

17. Prime
18. $(3x + 2)(2x - 5)$
19. $(x + 3y)(x - 4y)$
20. $4(x^2 + 16)$

21. $5x^3y(1 + 2x^2y + 3x^4y^2)$

# Elementary Algebra Review

# Unit 5

# Rational Expressions

**Simplify**

1. $\dfrac{x}{x^2 - x}$

2. $\dfrac{5x - 30}{x^2 - 36}$

3. $\dfrac{x^2 - 81}{x^2 - 10x + 9}$

**Multiply or divide as indicated**

4. $\dfrac{x^2 - 49}{x^2 - 9x + 14} \bullet \dfrac{x + 2}{x + 7}$

5. $\dfrac{x^2 - 4}{x^2 - 2x} \bullet \dfrac{x}{x^2 + 7x + 10}$

6. $\dfrac{3x + 9}{x} \bullet \dfrac{x^2 - 5x + 6}{x^2 - 9}$

7. $\dfrac{2x^2 + 5x + 3}{x^2 + 2x + 1} \bullet \dfrac{x^3}{2x^2 + 3x}$

8. $\dfrac{x - 3}{x^2 - 25} \div \dfrac{x^2 - 9}{x^2 + 8x + 15}$

9. $\dfrac{x^2}{x^2 - 4x - 12} \div \dfrac{x^2 - 2x}{x^2 - 4}$

10. $\dfrac{x^2 - 64}{x^2 + 10x + 16} \div \dfrac{x^2 - 9x + 8}{x^2 + 2x}$

11. $\dfrac{3x^2 - 8x + 5}{6x - 10} \div \dfrac{x^2 - 3x + 2}{x^2 - 4}$

**Add or Subtract as indicated**

12. $\dfrac{1}{x} - \dfrac{2}{y}$

13. $\dfrac{x}{x^2-49} + \dfrac{7}{x^2-49}$

14. $\dfrac{3}{x} + \dfrac{4}{x+3}$

15. $\dfrac{3}{x+5} - \dfrac{x}{x^2-25}$

16. $\dfrac{3}{x-3} + \dfrac{6}{x^2-8x+15}$

17. $\dfrac{5}{x^2-3x} - \dfrac{5}{x^2-9}$

**What values for x should be excluded?**

18. $\dfrac{x}{(x-2)(2x+3)}$

19. $\dfrac{x+2}{x^2-64}$

$(x-8)(x+8)$
$x-8=0 \quad \big| \quad x+8=0$
$x=8 \quad \big| \quad x=-8$

20. $\dfrac{7}{2x^2-5x-3}$

**Solve the following equations for x**

21. $\dfrac{1}{x} + \dfrac{3}{5} = -3$

$\dfrac{1}{x} + \dfrac{3}{5} = \dfrac{-3}{5x}$

$1(5) + 3x = -3(5x)$
$5 + 3x = -15x \qquad x = \dfrac{-5}{18}$
$15x + 3x = -5$
$18x = -5$

22. $\dfrac{3}{x-3} + \dfrac{2}{x-4} = \dfrac{7}{x^2-7x+12}$

$\dfrac{3}{x-3} + \dfrac{2}{x-4} = \dfrac{7}{(x-3)(x-4)}$

$3(x-4) + 2(x-3) = 7$
$3x-12 + 2x-6 = 7$
$3x+2x = 7+12+6$
$5x = 25$
$\dfrac{5x}{5} = \dfrac{25}{5}$
$x = 5$

23. $\dfrac{2}{x} + \dfrac{3x}{x+3} = \dfrac{3x^2}{x^2+3x}$

$\dfrac{2}{x} + \dfrac{3x}{x+3} = \dfrac{3x^2}{x(x+3)} \quad \text{CD}$

$\dfrac{2(x+3)}{x} + 3x(x) = 3x^2$

$2x+6 + 3x^2 = 3x^2$
$2x+6 + 3x^2 - 3x^2 = 0$
$2x+6 = 0$
$2x = -6$
$x = -3$

24. $\dfrac{3}{x-3} + \dfrac{x}{x^2-9} = \dfrac{5}{x+3}$

$\dfrac{3}{x-3} + \dfrac{x}{(x-3)(x+3)} = \dfrac{5}{(x+3)}$

$3(x+3) + x = 5(x-3)$
$3x+9 + x = 5x-15$
$3x+x-5x = -9-15$
$-x = -24$
$\dfrac{-x}{-1} = \dfrac{-24}{-1}$
$x = 24$

51

# Unit 5
## Review Form B

**Simplify**

1. $\dfrac{x}{x^2 + x}$

2. $\dfrac{3x - 12}{x^2 - 16}$

3. $\dfrac{x^2 - 49}{x^2 - 8x + 7}$

**Multiply or divide as indicated**

4. $\dfrac{x^2 - 64}{x^2 - 13x + 40} \bullet \dfrac{x - 5}{x - 7}$

5. $\dfrac{x^2 - 9}{x^2 - 3x} \bullet \dfrac{x}{x^2 + 9x + 18}$

6. $\dfrac{4x + 16}{x} \bullet \dfrac{x^2 - 8x + 16}{x^2 - 16}$

7. $\dfrac{5x^2 + 7x + 2}{x^2 + 3x + 2} \bullet \dfrac{x^3}{5x^2 + 2x}$

8. $\dfrac{x + 5}{x^2 - 49} \div \dfrac{x^2 - 25}{x^2 + 2x - 35}$

9. $\dfrac{x^2}{x^2 + 4x - 12} \div \dfrac{x^2 - 6x}{x^2 - 36}$

10. $\dfrac{x^2 - 81}{x^2 + 6x - 27} \div \dfrac{x^2 - 10x + 9}{x^2 - 3x}$

11. $\dfrac{5x^2 + 11x + 2}{2x + 16} \div \dfrac{x^2 - 6x - 16}{x^2 - 64}$

**Add or Subtract as indicated**

12.  $\dfrac{x}{7} + \dfrac{y}{5}$

13.  $\dfrac{x}{x^2 - 81} - \dfrac{9}{x^2 - 81}$

14.  $\dfrac{2}{x} + \dfrac{7}{x - 2}$

15.  $\dfrac{4}{x + 6} + \dfrac{x}{x^2 - 36}$

16.  $\dfrac{2}{x - 4} - \dfrac{2}{x^2 - 7x + 12}$

17.  $\dfrac{7}{x^2 - 5x} - \dfrac{7}{x^2 - 25}$

**What values for x should be excluded?**

18.  $\dfrac{x}{(x - 3)(2x + 5)}$

19.  $\dfrac{x + 3}{x^2 - 81}$

20.  $\dfrac{5}{3x^2 - 8x + 5}$

**Solve the following equations for x**

21.  $\dfrac{1}{x} + \dfrac{2}{3} = -5$

22.  $\dfrac{5}{x - 5} + \dfrac{3}{x - 3} = \dfrac{2}{x^2 - 8x + 15}$

23.  $\dfrac{3}{x} + \dfrac{5x}{x + 7} = \dfrac{5x^2}{x^2 + 7x}$

24.  $\dfrac{5}{x - 1} + \dfrac{x}{x^2 - 1} = \dfrac{7}{x + 1}$

**Simplify**

1. $\dfrac{x^2}{x^2-2x}$
   A. $-\dfrac{1}{2x}$
   B. $\dfrac{x}{x-2}$
   C. $x-2$
   D. $-2x$

2. $\dfrac{8x-4}{4x^2-4x+1}$
   A. $\dfrac{4}{2x-1}$
   B. $\dfrac{4x-2}{2x-1}$
   C. $\dfrac{2x-1}{x^2-x+1}$
   D. $\dfrac{2}{x-1}$

**Perform the indicated operation, then simplify if possible**

3. $\dfrac{3}{x}-\dfrac{5}{y}$
   A. $-\dfrac{2}{x+y}$
   B. $\dfrac{3y-5x}{x+y}$
   C. $\dfrac{3y-5x}{xy}$
   D. $-\dfrac{2}{xy}$

4. $\dfrac{2}{x}+\dfrac{3}{x+5}$
   A. $\dfrac{5}{2x+5}$
   B. $\dfrac{5}{x(x+5)}$
   C. $\dfrac{5x+5}{x(x+5)}$
   D. $\dfrac{5x+10}{x(x+5)}$

5. $\dfrac{5}{x+3}-\dfrac{3}{x}$
   A. $\dfrac{2x-9}{x(x+3)}$
   B. $\dfrac{2x-3}{x(x+3)}$
   C. $\dfrac{2x+9}{x(x+3)}$
   D. $\dfrac{2x+3}{x(x+3)}$

6. $\dfrac{3x^2}{x^2+9x+8}\bullet\dfrac{x^2-64}{x^2-8x}$
   A. $\dfrac{3x^2}{x(x+1)}$
   B. $\dfrac{3x}{x+1}$
   C. $\dfrac{24}{x(3x+8)}$
   D. $3$

**Solve for x**

7. $\frac{1}{4}(x+3)=2$    A. −1    B. −10    C. −5    D. 5

8. $\frac{3}{x+5}=\frac{5}{x+2}$    A. $\frac{3}{2}$    B. $-\frac{19}{2}$    C. $-\frac{3}{2}$    D. $\frac{19}{2}$

9. $\frac{2}{x}+10=\frac{3}{x}$    A. $\frac{1}{2}$    B. $\frac{1}{10}$    C. $-\frac{1}{2}$    D. $-\frac{1}{10}$

10. $\frac{5}{2}+\frac{3}{x}=-4$    A. −2    B. $\frac{2}{5}$    C. $-\frac{13}{6}$    D. $-\frac{6}{13}$

11. $\frac{4}{x+3}=\frac{3}{x+7}$    A. 4    B. −19    C. −4    D. 19

12. $\frac{5}{x}+8=\frac{3}{x}$    A. 4    B. −4    C. $-\frac{1}{4}$    D. $\frac{1}{4}$

13. $\frac{3}{2}+\frac{5}{x}=-6$    A. $-\frac{2}{3}$    B. $\frac{2}{3}$    C. $-\frac{16}{3}$    D. $-\frac{22}{3}$

**Answers to Unit 5, Review Form A**

1. $\dfrac{1}{x-1}$    2. $\dfrac{5}{x+6}$    3. $\dfrac{x+9}{x-1}$    4. $\dfrac{x+2}{x-2}$    5. $\dfrac{1}{x+5}$

6. $\dfrac{3(x-2)}{x}$    7. $\dfrac{x^2}{x+1}$    8. $\dfrac{1}{x-5}$    9. $\dfrac{x}{x-6}$    10. $\dfrac{x}{x-1}$

11. $\dfrac{x+2}{2}$    12. $\dfrac{y-2x}{xy}$    13. $\dfrac{1}{x-7}$    14. $\dfrac{7x+9}{x(x+3)}$    15. $\dfrac{2x-15}{(x+5)(x-5)}$

16. $\dfrac{3}{x-5}$    17. $\dfrac{15}{x(x-3)(x+3)}$    18. $2, -\dfrac{3}{2}$    19. 8, -8    20. $3, -\dfrac{1}{2}$

21. $-\dfrac{5}{18}$    22. 5    23. No solution    24. 24

**Answers to Unit 5, Review Form B**

1. $\dfrac{1}{x+1}$    2. $\dfrac{3}{x+4}$    3. $\dfrac{x+7}{x-1}$    4. $\dfrac{x+8}{x-7}$    5. $\dfrac{1}{x+6}$

6. $\dfrac{4(x-4)}{x}$    7. $\dfrac{x^2}{x+2}$    8. $\dfrac{1}{x-7}$    9. $\dfrac{x}{x-2}$    10. $\dfrac{x}{x-1}$

11. $\dfrac{5x+1}{2}$    12. $\dfrac{5x+7y}{35}$    13. $\dfrac{1}{x+9}$    14. $\dfrac{9x-4}{x(x-2)}$    15. $\dfrac{5x-24}{(x+6)(x-6)}$

16. $\dfrac{2}{x-3}$    17. $\dfrac{35}{x(x-5)(x+5)}$    18. $3, -\dfrac{5}{2}$    19. 9, -9    20. $1, \dfrac{5}{3}$

21. $-\dfrac{3}{17}$    22. 4    23. No solution    24. 12

**Answers to Unit 6, Multiple Choice Review Form C**

1. B   2. A   3. C   4. D   5. A   6. B   7. D
8. B   9. B   10. D   11. B   12. C   13. A

# Elementary Algebra Review

# Unit 6

# Graphing

# Unit 6
## Review Form A

1. Complete the ordered pairs so that each is a solution for $2x - y = 5$.
   (0, )    ( ,0)    (2, )    ( ,5)

2. Complete the ordered pairs so that each is a solution for $3x + 4y = 12$.
   (0, )    ( ,0)    ( ,4)    (3, )

3. Find four solutions for $2x - 3y = 6$.

4. Find three solutions for $x = 5$

5. Graph    $x + y = -2$

6. Graph    $y = 4x$

7. Graph    $3y = x$

8. Graph    $y = \dfrac{3}{4}x + 2$

9. Graph    $y = \dfrac{-2}{3}x + 1$

10. Graph    $x + 3y = 6$

11. Graph    $-2x + 3y = 21$

12. Graph    $x - 4y = -8$

13. Graph    $2x - y = 8$

14. Graph    $3x + y = -2$

15. Graph    $x = -3$

16. Graph    $y = 7$

# Unit 6
## Review Form B

1. Complete the ordered pairs so that each is a solution for $3x - y = 7$.
   (0, )   ( ,0)   (2, )   ( ,5)

2. Complete the ordered pairs so that each is a solution for $2x + 3y = 6$.
   (0, )   ( ,0)   ( ,4)   (5, )

3. Find four solutions for $3x - 4y = 12$.

4. Find three solutions for $y = 3$

5. Graph   $x + y = -5$

6. Graph   $4y = x$

7. Graph   $y = 2x$

8. Graph   $y = \dfrac{3}{5}x + 1$

9. Graph   $y = \dfrac{-3}{4} + 2$

10. Graph   $x + 4y = 8$

11. Graph   $-7x + y = 2$

12. Graph   $x - 3y = -6$

13. Graph   $3x - y = 6$

14. Graph   $2x + y = -5$

15. Graph   $x = 5$

16. Graph   $y = -4$

# Unit 6
## Multiple Choice Review Form C

1. Which is a solution for the equation 7x - 2y = 8?
     a) (3,2)          b) (2,2)          c) (2,3)          d) (3,3)

2. Which of the equations has (1,-2), (5,2) and (-7,-10) as solutions?
     a) x + y = 2       b) x - y = 2       c) x + y = 3       d) x - y = 3

3. Which equation matches this graph?
     a) x = 2          b) x + y = 2
     c) y = 2          d) x - y = 2

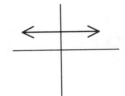

4. Which equation matches this graph?
     a) x + y = 3       b) x = 3y
     c) y = 3x         d) x = 3

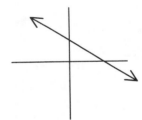

5. Which of the following graphs represent the equation y = ½ x?

  a)               b)               c)               d)

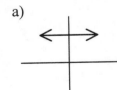  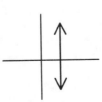 

6. Which of the following graphs shows a line have an equation y = x + 3?

  a)               b)               c)               d)

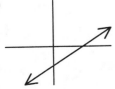 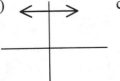 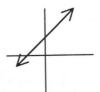 

7. Which of the following graphs represent the equation y = 3x – 2?

a)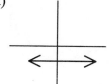

b)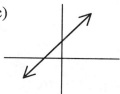

c)

d)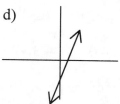

8. Which of the following points lies in the fourth quadrant?

a)

b)

c)

d)

9. Which of the following graphs represent the equation 2x + 3y = 6?

a)

b)

c)

d)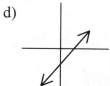

10. Which of the following graphs represent the equation 4x – 5y = 10?

a)

b)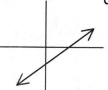

c)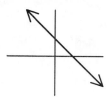

d)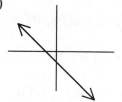

61

**Answers to Unit 6, Review Form A**

1. (0,-5)    (5/2,0)    (2,-1)    (5,5)

2. (0,3)    (4,0)    (-4/3,4)    (3,3/4)

3. Just a few of the possibilities:  (0,-2)  (3,0)  (6,2)  (-3,-4)

4. Just a few of the possibilities:  (5,0)  (5,3)  (5,-7)

5.

6.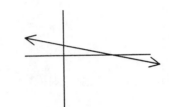

7.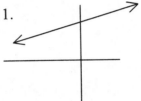

8.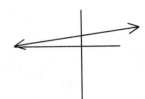

9.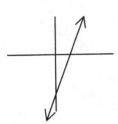

10.

11.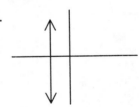

12.

13.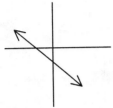

14.

15.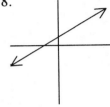

16.

**Answers to Unit 6, Review Form B**

1. (0,-7)    (7/3,0)    (2,-1)    (4,5)

2. (0,2)    (3,0)    (-3,4)    (5,-4/3)

3. Just a few of the possibilities:  (0,-3)  (4,0)  (-4,-6)  (8,3)

4. Just a few of the possibilities:  (0,3)  (5,3)  (-2,3)

5.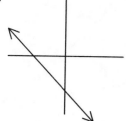

6.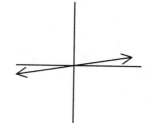

7.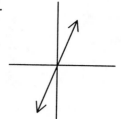

8.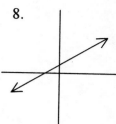

9.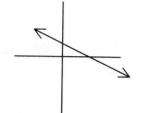

10.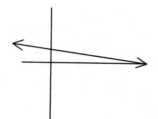

11.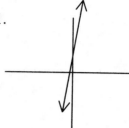

12.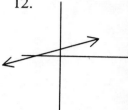

13.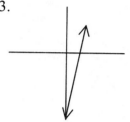

14.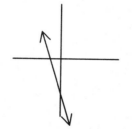

15.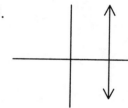

16.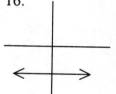

**Answers to Unit 6, Multiple Choice Review Form C**

1. C

2. D

3. C

4. A

5. B

6. C

7. D

8. D

9. A

10. B

# Elementary Algebra Review

# Unit 7

# Systems of Equations

1. Solve by graphing: $2x + y = 8$
$y = 4$

2. Solve by graphing: $x - y = 4$
$2x + 3y = 3$

3. Solve for x: $4x + 2y = 0$
$3x + y = 1$

4. Solve for y: $2x - 3y = -19$
$3x + 5y = 0$

5. Solve for x and y: $2x - 1 = y$
$3x + 2y = 26$

6. Solve for x and y: $x = 4y + 9$
$2x + y = 9$

7. Solve for x and y: $2x - 5y = -16$
$3x + 4y = -1$

**Solve the following applications:**

8. The sum of two numbers is 15. Five times the smaller is three more than the larger. Find the two numbers.

9. One number is one less than twice another number. The sum of the two numbers is -10. Find the two numbers.

10. John wanted to cash a check for $195 and asked the bank teller for $5 and $10 bills. He received 22 bills. How many of each kind was he given?

11. Tammy purchased 40 stamps in 15¢ and 25¢ denominations. The total cost of the stamps was $6.90. Find how many 25¢ stamps were purchased.

12. Four hundred twenty tickets were sold for a CCC theater production. Student tickets cost $5 and non-student tickets cost $7. If the ticket booth collected a total of $2460, how many of each kind of ticket was sold?

13. A pharmacist has a 15% saline solution and a 45% saline solution. How much of each solution should be used to form 120 centiliters (cL) of a 35% saline solution?

14. Bill has invested $43,000, part is invested in his company which yields 16% and the remainder in bonds yielding 6%. If he earns $5,500 in interest for one year, how much does he have invested at each rate?

## Unit 7
## Review Form B

1. Solve by graphing: $2x - y = 1$
$x = 3$

2. Solve by graphing: $x + y = 3$
$x - y = 7$

3. Solve for x: $5x + 2y = -4$
$x + y = 1$

4. Solve for y: $3x + 4y = 8$
$-2x - 5y = -3$

5. Solve for x and y: $y = -3x - 7$
$4x - 2y = 14$

6. Solve for x and y: $4x - 2 = y$
$x + 3y = 20$

7. Solve for x and y: $2x + 3y = -15$
$5x - 2y = -47$

**Solve the following applications:**

8. The sum of two numbers is 19. Twenty-two more than the smaller is one less than the larger. Find the two numbers.

9. One number is one less than twice another number. The sum of the two numbers is 14. Find the two numbers.

10. Ken wanted to cash a check for $175 and asked the bank teller for $5 and $10 bills. He received 21 bills. How many of each kind was he given?

11. Christie purchased 49 stamps in 20¢ and 25¢ denominations. The total cost of the stamps was $10.25. Find how many 20¢ stamps were purchased.

12. Two hundred forty tickets were sold for a CCC basketball game. Student tickets cost $3 and non-student tickets cost $4.50. If the ticket booth collected a total of $885, how many of each kind of ticket was sold?

13. A chemist wishes to combine a 10% acid solution with a 60% acid solution to form 150 milliliters (mL) of a 35% acid solution. How much of each solution should be used?

15. Betty has $35,000 invested. Part of her money is in a CD which pays 8% annually and part is in a savings account which pays 5% annually. If she earns $2,530 in interest, what is the amount in each account?

1. Solve by graphing:   x + y = 3
                                    x = 3

a) 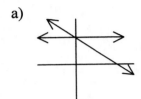   b) 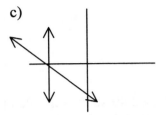   c) 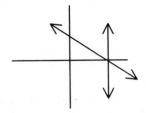   d)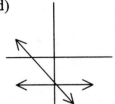

2. Solve by graphing:   2x - y = 3
                                     3x + y = 2

a) 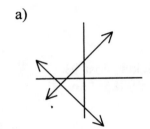   b) 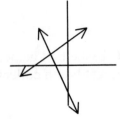   c) 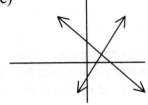   d)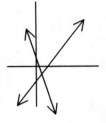

3. Solve for x:        3x - 2y = -12
                               5x +  y = -7

a) x = -1            b) x = -2            c) x = 3            d) x = -3

4. Solve for y:        x - 2y = 9
                               3x - 4y = 19

a) y = 4            b) y = -1            c) y = -4            d) y = 1

5. Solve for x and y:    3x - 2y = 7
                                   -x + 3y = 7

a) (4,3)            b) (5,3)            c) (5,4)            d) (4,5)

6. Solve for x and y:  $5x - 2y = 8$
$3x + 4y = 10$

a) (2,1)          b) (1,2)          c) (0,2)          d) (-2,1)

7. The sum of two numbers is -7.  Four times the smaller is one less than five times the larger.  Find the two numbers.

a) 2 and -9          b) -4 and -2          c) 3 and 4          d) -3 and -4

8. A laboratory has a 60% hydrochloric acid solution and a 20% hydrochloric acid solution.  How much of each of the two solutions should be used to produce 200 milliliters (mL) of a 35% acid solution?

a) 70 mL of 20%          b) 75 mL of 60%          c) 85 mL of 20%          d) 90 mL of 60%
130 mL of 60%          125 mL of 20%          115 mL of 60%          110 mL of 20%

9. 330 tickets were sold for the bus trip to D.C.  Student tickets were $15 and non-student tickets were $18.  The Student Activities office collected $5505.  Find how many student tickets were sold?

a) 135          b) 140          c) 145          d) 150

10. Cindy has $30,000 invested in two different stocks.  One yields 7% and the other 9% per year.  If she earns $2460 in interest for one year, how much does she have invested at each rate?

a) $12,000 at 9%          b) $16,000 at 7%          c) $18,000 at 9%          d) $16,000 at 9%
$18,000 at 7%          $14,000 at 9%          $12,000 at 7%          $14,000 at 7%

71

**Answers to Unit 7, Review Form A**

1. (2,4)

2. (3,-1)

3. x = 1

4. y = 3

5. (4,7)

6. (5,-1)

7. (-3,2)

8. smaller = 3
   larger = 12

9. (-7,-3)

10. 5 of $5
    17 of $10

11. 9

12. 240 of $5
    180 of $7

13. 40 cL of 15% soln.
    80 cL of 45% soln.

14. $29,200 at 16%
    $13,800 at 6%

**Answers to Unit 7, Review Form B**

1. (3,5)

2. (5,-2)

3. x = -2

4. y = -1

5. (0,-7)

6. (2,6)

7. (-9,1)

8. smaller = -2
   larger = 21

9. (5,9)

10. 7 of $5
    14 of $10

11. 40

12. 130 of $3
    110 of $4.50

13. 75 mL of 10% soln.
    75 mL of 60% soln.

14. $26,000 at 8%
    $ 9,000 at 5%

**Answers to Unit 7, Multiple Choice Review Form C**

1. B

2. D

3. B

4. C

5. C

6. A

7. D

8. B

9. C

10. C

# Elementary Algebra Review

# Unit 8

# Radical Expressions

Unit 8
Review Form A

**In each of the following, simplify the radical forms:**

1. a) $\sqrt{81}$      b) $\dfrac{\sqrt{36}}{\sqrt{49}}$      c) $\sqrt{144}$      d) $\sqrt{196}$

2. a) $\sqrt{54}$      b) $\sqrt{48}$      c) $\sqrt{50}$      d) $\sqrt{20}$

3. a) $\sqrt{108}$      b) $\sqrt{98}$      c) $-\sqrt{125}$      d) $-\sqrt{96}$

4. a) $\sqrt{g^2}$      b) $\sqrt{z^4}$      c) $\sqrt{36r^2}$      d) $\sqrt{100s^6t^8}$

5. a) $\sqrt{2a^3}$      b) $\sqrt{7xy^3}$      c) $\sqrt{5c^5d^4}$      d) $\sqrt{14m^7n^9}$

6. a) $\sqrt{27b^5}$      b) $\sqrt{80d^9}$      c) $\sqrt{72x^4y^7}$      d) $\sqrt{162ab^5}$

**Perform the following operations and combine like terms.**

7. a) $5\sqrt{3}+8\sqrt{3}$      b) $2\sqrt{16}+5\sqrt{16}$      c) $2\sqrt{32}+3\sqrt{32}+\sqrt{32}$

8. a) $4\sqrt{12}+2\sqrt{3}$      b) $\sqrt{80x^3}+x\sqrt{5x}$      c) $2\sqrt{27}+4\sqrt{108}+2\sqrt{20}$

74

9. a) $3\sqrt{2} - 5\sqrt{2}$     b) $7\sqrt{9} - 3\sqrt{9}$     c) $4\sqrt{12} - 2\sqrt{12} - \sqrt{12}$

10. a) $5\sqrt{45} - 2\sqrt{5}$     b) $y\sqrt{96y} - \sqrt{6y^3}$     c) $3\sqrt{72} - \sqrt{162} - \sqrt{18}$

11. a) $3\sqrt{12}\,\sqrt{2}$     b) $\sqrt{27}\,\sqrt{3}$     c) $\sqrt{5x}\,\sqrt{3xy^2}$     d) $(2\sqrt{5})^2$

12. a) $3(\sqrt{2} - 1)$     b) $\sqrt{5}(2 + \sqrt{3})$     c) $(\sqrt{5} + x)(\sqrt{3} - x)$     d) $(\sqrt{3} + 2)(\sqrt{3} - 2)$

13. a) $(\sqrt{10})^2$     b. $(-4\sqrt{5})^2$     c) $(2\sqrt{2x})^2$     d) $7(\sqrt{3a^4})^2$

14. a) $(\sqrt{2} + a)^2$     b) $(2 - \sqrt{5})^2$     c) $(\sqrt{7} + \sqrt{2})^2$     d) $(3 - 4\sqrt{2})^2$

**Find the missing sides of the right triangle.  Simplify radical forms where possible.**

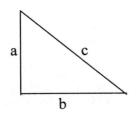

15.  If a = 3 and b = 6, then c =

16.  If b = 4 and c = 5, then a =

17.  If a = 5 and c = 20, then b =

18.  If a = 2 and b = 3, then c =

19.  A 12 foot ladder is placed against a building to a window 8 feet above the ground.
     What is the distance from the base of the building to the base of the ladder?

20.  Find the length of a ramp used to roll barrels up to a loading dock which is 6 feet high
     and 8 feet away from the base of the ramp.

21.  The sun's rays cast an 8 foot shadow on the ground from an 12 foot tree.  Find the
     distance from the top of the tree to the end of the shadow on the ground.

**In each of the following, simplify the radical forms:**

1. a) $\sqrt{64}$      b) $\sqrt{\dfrac{49}{81}}$      c) $\sqrt{225}$      d) $\sqrt{169}$

2. a) $\sqrt{12}$      b) $\sqrt{75}$      c) $\sqrt{45}$      d) $\sqrt{28}$

3. a) $\sqrt{72}$      b) $\sqrt{147}$      c) $-\sqrt{150}$      d) $-\sqrt{80}$

4. a) $\sqrt{4c^2}$      b) $\sqrt{x^6}$      c) $\sqrt{25s^8}$      d) $\sqrt{121p^{10}q^4}$

5. a) $\sqrt{2b^5}$      b) $\sqrt{6y^3z}$      c) $\sqrt{10g^6h^5}$      d) $\sqrt{16p^{11}q^{13}}$

6. a) $\sqrt{45c^7}$      b) $\sqrt{48a^5}$      c) $\sqrt{50r^3s^4}$      d) $\sqrt{27mn^9}$

**Perform the following operations and combine like terms.**

7. a) $3\sqrt{2}+5\sqrt{2}$      b) $7\sqrt{9}+3\sqrt{9}$      c) $4\sqrt{12}+2\sqrt{12}+\sqrt{12}$

8. a) $5\sqrt{45}+2\sqrt{5}$      b) $y\sqrt{96y}+\sqrt{6y^3}$      c) $3\sqrt{72}+\sqrt{162}+\sqrt{18}$

9. a) $5\sqrt{3} - 8\sqrt{3}$     b) $2\sqrt{16} - 5\sqrt{16}$     c) $2\sqrt{32} - 3\sqrt{32} - \sqrt{32}$

10. a) $4\sqrt{12} - 2\sqrt{12}$     b) $x\sqrt{5x} - \sqrt{80x^3}$     c) $2\sqrt{27} - 4\sqrt{108} - 2\sqrt{20}$

11. a) $3\sqrt{15}\sqrt{3}$     b) $\sqrt{24}\sqrt{6}$     c) $\sqrt{6x^2y}\sqrt{3y^3}$     d) $2(\sqrt{7})^2$

12. a) $2(\sqrt{5} - 1)$     b) $\sqrt{7}(3 + \sqrt{2})$     c) $(\sqrt{3} + x)(\sqrt{2} - x)$     d) $(\sqrt{6} + 7)(\sqrt{6} - 7)$

13. a) $(\sqrt{12})^2$     b) $(-3\sqrt{6})^2$     c) $(4\sqrt{2x^5})^2$     d) $(2\sqrt{3b^8})^2$

14. a) $(\sqrt{3} + 2)^2$     b) $(b - \sqrt{7})^2$     c) $(\sqrt{6} + \sqrt{2})^2$     d) $(5 - 2\sqrt{6})^2$

**Find the missing sides of the right triangle. Simplify radical forms where possible.**

15. If a = 6 and c = 9, then b =

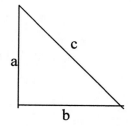

16. If b = 5 and c = 8, then a =

17. If a = 2 and b = 6, then c =

18. If b = 1 and c = 2, then a =

19. Find the altitudes for each of the following triangles:

a.

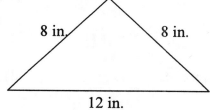

8 in.    8 in.

12 in.

b.

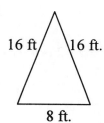

16 ft    16 ft.

8 ft.

20. If you travel 10 miles west and then 15 miles south, how far are you from your starting point?

21. If a 25 foot guy wire is supporting a 20 foot flag pole, find the distance from the pole that the guy wire is to be driven into the ground.

# Unit 8
## Multiple Choice Review Form C

1. Evaluate: $-\sqrt{169}$     a) -13, 13     b) $-13$     c) 13     d) $-13^2$

2. Simplify: $\sqrt{\dfrac{81}{121}}$

    a) ¾     b) 8/11     c) 9/13     d) 9/11

3. Simplify: $\sqrt{10a^2b^3}$

    a) $ab\sqrt{10b}$     b) $a\sqrt{10b^3}$     c) $b\sqrt{10a^2b}$     d) $5ab\sqrt{b}$

✗ 4. Simplify: $(3a\sqrt{4a})^2$

$(3a\sqrt{4a})(3a\sqrt{4a})$
$(9a^2)(4a)$
$36 \cdot a^2 \cdot a$
$36a^3$

    a) $12a^2$     b) $36a^3$     c) $36a^2$     d) $48a^3$

5. Simplify: $2\sqrt{3} + 3\sqrt{3} - \sqrt{3}$

    a) $6\sqrt{3}$     b) $5\sqrt{3}$     c) $4\sqrt{3}$     d) $\sqrt{3}$

6. Simplify: $5\sqrt{8} + 7\sqrt{2} - 4\sqrt{18}$

    a) $8\sqrt{8}$     b) $5\sqrt{2}$     c) $8\sqrt{-8}$     d) $2\sqrt{5}$

✗ 7. Simplify: $(3\sqrt{2x})^2$

$(3\sqrt{2x})(3\sqrt{2x})$
$(3 \cdot 3)(\sqrt{2x} \cdot \sqrt{2x})$
$(9)(2x)$
$18x$

    a) $9\sqrt{2x}$     b) $6\sqrt{2x}$     c) 6x     d) 18x

8. Simplify: $2\sqrt{3}(4\sqrt{2} - \sqrt{3})$

    a) $8\sqrt{5} - 2\sqrt{6}$     b) $8\sqrt{6} - 6$     c) $8\sqrt{6} - 18$     d) $6\sqrt{5} - 2\sqrt{6}$

9. Simplify: $(5 - 2\sqrt{3})(5 + 2\sqrt{3})$

    a) 13     b) $25 - 4\sqrt{3}$     c) 37     d) $25 + 4\sqrt{3}$

10. Simplify: $(2 - 3\sqrt{7})^2$

    a) $4 + 9\sqrt{7}$     b) $4 - 12\sqrt{7}$     c) $67 - 12\sqrt{7}$     d) $4 - 9\sqrt{7}$

## Answers to Unit 8, Review Form A

1. a) 9     b) $\dfrac{6}{7}$     c) 12     d) 14

2. a) $3\sqrt{6}$     b) $4\sqrt{3}$     c) $5\sqrt{2}$     d) $2\sqrt{5}$

3. a) $6\sqrt{3}$     b) $7\sqrt{2}$     c) $-5\sqrt{5}$     d) $-4\sqrt{6}$

4. a) $g$     b) $z^2$     c) $6r$     d) $10s^3t^4$

5. a) $a\sqrt{2a}$     b) $y\sqrt{7xy}$     c) $c^2d^2\sqrt{5c}$     d) $m^3n^4\sqrt{14mn}$

6. a) $3b^2\sqrt{3b}$     b) $4d^4\sqrt{5d}$     c) $6x^2y^3\sqrt{2y}$     d) $9b^2\sqrt{2ab}$

7. a) $13\sqrt{3}$     b) 28     c) $24\sqrt{2}$

8. a) $10\sqrt{3}$     b) $5x\sqrt{5x}$     c) $30\sqrt{3}+4\sqrt{5}$

9. a) $-2\sqrt{2}$     b) 12     c) $2\sqrt{3}$

10. a) $13\sqrt{5}$     b) $3y\sqrt{6y}$     c) $6\sqrt{2}$

11. a) $6\sqrt{6}$     b) 9     c) $xy\sqrt{15}$     d) 20

12. a) $3\sqrt{2}-3$     b) $2\sqrt{5}+\sqrt{15}$     c) $\sqrt{15}-x\sqrt{5}+x\sqrt{3}-x^2$     d) $-1$

13. a) 10     b) 80     c) $8x$     d) $21a^4$

14. a) $2+2a\sqrt{2}+a^2$     b) $9-4\sqrt{5}$     c) $9+2\sqrt{14}$     d) $41-24\sqrt{2}$

15. $3\sqrt{5}$     16. 3     17. $5\sqrt{15}$     18. $\sqrt{13}$

19. $4\sqrt{5}$ feet     20. 10 feet     21. $2\sqrt{52}$ feet

# Answers to Unit 8, Review Form B

1. a) 8      b) 7/9      c) 15      d) 13

2. a) $2\sqrt{3}$      b) $5\sqrt{3}$      c) $3\sqrt{5}$      d) $2\sqrt{7}$

3. a) $6\sqrt{2}$      b) $7\sqrt{3}$      c) $-5\sqrt{6}$      d) $-4\sqrt{5}$

4. a) $2c$      b) $x^3$      c) $5s^4$      d) $11p^5q^4$

5. a) $b^2\sqrt{2b}$      b) $y\sqrt{6yz}$      c) $g^3h^2\sqrt{10h}$      d) $4p^5q^6\sqrt{pq}$

6. a) $3c^3\sqrt{5c}$      b) $4a^2\sqrt{3a}$      c) $5rs^2\sqrt{2r}$      d) $3n^4\sqrt{3mn}$

7. a) $8\sqrt{2}$      b) 30      c) $14\sqrt{3}$

8. a) $17\sqrt{5}$      b) $5y\sqrt{6y}$      c) $30\sqrt{2}$

9. a) $-3\sqrt{3}$      b) $-12$      c) $-8\sqrt{2}$

10. a) $4\sqrt{3}$      b) $-3x\sqrt{5x}$      c) $-18\sqrt{3} - 4\sqrt{5}$

11. a) $9\sqrt{5}$      b) 12      c) $3xy^2\sqrt{2}$      d) 14

12. a) $2\sqrt{5} - 2$      b) $3\sqrt{7} + \sqrt{14}$      c) $6 - x\sqrt{3} + x\sqrt{2} - x^2$      d) $-43$

13. a) 12      b) 54      c) $32x^5$      d) $12b^8$

14. a) $7 + 4\sqrt{3}$      b) $b^2 - 2b\sqrt{7} + 7$      c) $8 + 4\sqrt{3}$      d) $49 - 20\sqrt{6}$

15. $3\sqrt{5}$      16. $\sqrt{39}$      17. $2\sqrt{10}$      18. $\sqrt{3}$

19. a) $2\sqrt{7}$ in.      20. $5\sqrt{13}$ miles      21. 15 feet      b) $4\sqrt{15}$ feet

# Answers to Unit 8, Multiple Choice Review Form C

1. B      4. B      7. D

2. D      5. C      8. B      10. C

3. A      6. B      9. A

# Elementary Algebra Review

# Comprehensive Review

# Comprehensive Review

For all problems 1-15, Solve for x

1. $2x + 10 = -5x$    a. $\dfrac{7}{10}$    b. $\dfrac{10}{7}$    c. $-\dfrac{10}{7}$    (d.) $-\dfrac{10}{3}$

2. $4x - 11 = 12x + 5$    a. $-2$    b. $2$    c. $1$    d. $-1$

3. $-2(x - 5) = -8$    a. $9$    b. $-9$    c. $\dfrac{3}{2}$    d. $-\dfrac{3}{2}$

4. $-5(x + 2) > 20$    a. $x > -6$    b. $x > 6$    c. $x < -6$    d. $x < 6$

5. $2x - 5 \le 4x - 7$    a. $x \ge 6$    b. $x \ge -1$    c. $x \le -1$    d. $x \ge 1$

6. $\dfrac{1}{x} + 5 = 10$    a. $5$    b. $\dfrac{1}{5}$    c. $\dfrac{1}{15}$    d. $15$

7. $\dfrac{x + 4}{2} = \dfrac{x - 3}{3}$    a. $5x + 6$    b. $\dfrac{5x + 6}{6}$    c. $-18$    d. $-7$

8. $\dfrac{2}{3}x + \dfrac{1}{2} = \dfrac{5}{6}x$    a. $3$    b. $-3$    c. $-\dfrac{6}{7}$    d. $\dfrac{6}{7}$

9. $\dfrac{1}{2}(x + 6) = 4$    a. $2$    b. $8$    c. $1$    d. $-4$

10. $\dfrac{3}{x + 2} + \dfrac{2}{x - 2} = \dfrac{5}{x^2 - 4}$    a. $1$    b. $\dfrac{7}{5}$    c. $\dfrac{3}{5}$    d. no solution

11. $y = mx + b$    a. $x = \dfrac{y}{mb}$    b. $x = \dfrac{y}{m + b}$    c. $x = \dfrac{y - m}{b}$    d. $x = \dfrac{y - b}{m}$

12. $w = 2x + 2y$    a. $x = w - y$    b. $x = \dfrac{w - 2y}{2}$    c. $x = \dfrac{w - 2}{2}$    d. $x = \dfrac{w}{2y}$

84

✳ 13. $x^2 - 144 = 0$     a. {12}     b. {-12}     c. {12, -12}     d. {72, -72}

✳ 14. $x^2 - 7x = -12$     a. {3, 4}     b. {-3, -4}     c. {3, -4}     d. {-3, 4}

✳ 15. $2x^2 - 3x = 5$     a. {1, -5}     b. {-1, 5}     c. $\left\{-1, \dfrac{5}{2}\right\}$     d. $\left\{-1, \dfrac{2}{5}\right\}$

✳ 16. Which of the following could be the graph of 2x – 3y = 12?

a.     b.

$y = mx + b$
$m = Rise/Run$

SAME SIDE MAKE
a  0 0

c.     d.

17. Which of the following could be the equation for the graph below?

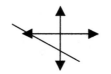

a. $y = \dfrac{1}{2}x - 3$     b. $y = -\dfrac{1}{2}x - 3$

c. $y = \dfrac{1}{2}x + 3$     d. $y = -\dfrac{1}{2} + 3$

✳ 18. Solve for x

$3x + y = 8$
$x + 2y = 1$

a. –1     b. 9     c. 3     d. $\dfrac{7}{3}$

✳ 19. Solve for x

$3x + y = 11$
$y = 2x + 1$

a. 5     b. 2     c. 6     d. $\dfrac{12}{5}$

20. If a = 2 and b = -3, then $3ab^2 - 2ab =$

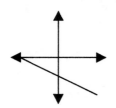

a. 42     b. –42     c. 66     d. –66

✳ 21. Evaluate $\dfrac{5 - 2x}{3x - 6}$ when x = -3     a. $-\dfrac{1}{15}$     b. $\dfrac{1}{15}$     c. $\dfrac{11}{15}$     d. $-\dfrac{11}{15}$

22. Evaluate: $-3x^2 - x + 5$
    when x = -2

    a. 39       b. 43       c. −9       d. −5

23. $(4x)^2$

    a. $4x^2$       b. $8x^2$       c. $16x^2$       d. $16x$

24. $(5x^4)(2x^8)$

    a. $10x^{12}$       b. $10x^7$       c. $7x^7$       d. $7x^{12}$

25. $\dfrac{x^8 y^{10}}{x^4 y^5}$

    a. $x^2 y^2$       b. $x^4 y^5$       c. $x^{12} y^{15}$       d. $x^2 y^5$

26. $\dfrac{21x^4 y^6}{14x^3 y^6}$

    a. $\dfrac{3xy}{2}$       b. $\dfrac{3}{2}$       c. $\dfrac{3x}{2}$       d. $7x$

27. $\dfrac{x^{-2} y^3}{x^2 y^{-5}}$

    a. $y^2$       b. $\dfrac{1}{y^2}$       c. $y^8$       d. $\dfrac{y^8}{x^4}$

28. $-7x^0$

    a. 0       b. 1       c. −1       d. −7

29. $-(5x - 4)$

    a. $-5x - 4$       b. $-5x + 4$       c. x       d. −x

30. $-3(4y + 5)$

    a. $-12y + 5$       b. $-12y + 15$       c. $-7y - 15$       d. $-12y - 15$

31. $3x + 5x - x$

    a. 8       b. $8x$       c. $7x$       d. $8x^2$

32. $(5a - b) - (3a - 4b)$

    a. $2a + 3b$       b. $2a - 5b$       c. $2a - 3b$       d. $8a - 5b$

33. $2x^2 + 3x^3$

    a. $5x^5$       b. $5x^6$       c. $5 + x^5$       d. can't combine

66-46 = 10
26 = 10
b = 5
$(-3)^2$    $-3^2$
9    -9

34. Subtract 5x − 7 from −3x + 2     a. −8x − 5     b. 2x − 5     c. −8x + 9     d. 2x − 9

35. |-7| - |2|     a. 9     b. 5     c. −9     d. −5

36. |-7 − 2|     a. 9     b. 5     c. −9     d. −5

37. Write 23,000 in scientific notation
  a. $23 \times 10^3$     b. $23 \times 10^{-3}$     c. $2.3 \times 10^4$     d. $2.3 \times 10^{-4}$

38. Write 0.00016 in scientific notation
  a. $16 \times 10^3$     b. $16 \times 10^{-3}$     c. $1.6 \times 10^4$     d. $1.6 \times 10^{-4}$

39. Write $5.1 \times 10^{-5}$ in standard notation
  a. 0.0000051     b. 0.000051     c. 5,100,000     d. 510,000

40. Evaluate $\dfrac{-8(-9) - 5^2}{5 - (-2)^2}$

  $-8(-9) = 25$     $\dfrac{72-25}{9} = -\dfrac{47}{9}$
  $5 - 4$

  a. 47     b. −97     c. $\dfrac{47}{9}$     d. $-\dfrac{97}{9}$

41. Multiply: $(5a − 2)^2$     a. $25a^2 − 4$     b. $25a^2 + 4$
  c. $25a^2 − 10a + 4$     d. $25a^2 − 20a + 4$

42. Multiply: $(2x − 3)(3x − 5)$     a. 5x − 8     b. $6x^2 + 15$
  c. $6x^2 − x + 15$     d. $6x^2 − 19x + 15$

43. Simplify: $\dfrac{4x^6 − 6x^3}{2x^4}$

  $\left(\dfrac{4x^6}{2x^4}\right) - \dfrac{6x^3}{2x^4}$

  $\dfrac{2x^2 - 3}{x}$

  a. $2x^3 − 3x$     b. $\dfrac{2x^2 − 3}{x}$     c. $2x^2 − \dfrac{3}{x}$     d. $2x^2 − 6x^3$

44. Divide: $x^2 − 6x − 7$ by x − 7     a. x − 1     b. x + 1     c. x − 13     d. x + 13
  (optional topic)

45. What is the remainder when $4x^2 − 6x + 7$ is divided by 2x − 1     (optional topic)

  a. −5     b. −9     c. 5     d. 9

46. Factor $x^2 - 10x - 24$

    a. $(x - 6)(x - 4)$          b. $(x - 12)(x + 2)$

    c. $(x - 6)(x + 4)$          d. $(x + 12)(x - 2)$

47. Factor $2x^2 - 5x - 7$

    a. $(2x + 1)(x - 7)$         b. $(2x - 7)(x + 1)$

    c. $(2x - 1)(x + 7)$         d. $(2x + 7)(x - 1)$

48. Which of the following is a factor of $81x^2 - 25$

    a. $9x - 25$      b. $x - 25$      c. $3x - 5$      d. $9x - 5$

49. Which of the following is a factor of $5x^2 - 3x - 2$

    a. $5x - 2$      b. $x - 2$      c. $x - 1$      d. $x + 1$

50. $\dfrac{5}{x} + \dfrac{4}{y}$

    a. $\dfrac{9}{xy}$      b. $\dfrac{9}{x+y}$      c. $\dfrac{5y+4x}{x+y}$      d. $\dfrac{5y+4x}{xy}$

51. $\dfrac{x}{5} + \dfrac{x}{7}$

    a. $\dfrac{2x}{12}$      b. $\dfrac{2x}{35}$      c. $\dfrac{12x^2}{35}$      d. $\dfrac{12x}{35}$

52. $\dfrac{1}{x} + \dfrac{4}{x+5}$

    a. $\dfrac{5}{2x+5}$      b. $\dfrac{5}{x^2+5x}$      c. $\dfrac{5x+5}{x^2+5x}$      d. $\dfrac{5x+5}{2x+5}$

53. $\dfrac{2}{x-3} + \dfrac{3}{x^2-8x+15}$

    a. $\dfrac{5}{x^2-7x-12}$      b. $\dfrac{5}{x^2-8x+15}$      c. $\dfrac{2x-1}{x^2-8x+15}$      d. $\dfrac{2x-7}{x^2-8x+15}$

54. $\dfrac{x}{x^2-4x}$

    a. $x^2 - 4$      b. $\dfrac{1}{x^2-4}$      c. $x - 4$      d. $\dfrac{1}{x-4}$

55. $\dfrac{2x-6}{x^2-9}$

    a. $\dfrac{2}{x-3}$      b. $\dfrac{2}{x+3}$      c. $\dfrac{2x-2}{x^2-3}$      d. can't simplify

56. $\dfrac{x+3}{x^2-9} \bullet \dfrac{x^2-5x+6}{x^2-4}$

    a. $x + 2$      b. $\dfrac{1}{x+2}$      c. $x - 2$      d. $\dfrac{1}{x-2}$

57. $\dfrac{x^2-49}{2x-14} \div \dfrac{3x^2+21x}{4x}$    a. $\dfrac{2}{3}$    b. $\dfrac{3}{2}$    c. $\dfrac{3(x+7)}{8}$    d. $\dfrac{3(x+7)^2}{8}$

58. $\sqrt{72}$    a. 36    b. $36\sqrt{2}$    c. $3\sqrt{8}$    d. $6\sqrt{2}$

59. $2\sqrt{2}+8\sqrt{2}-\sqrt{2}$    a. 10    b. $10\sqrt{2}$    c. $9\sqrt{6}$    d. $9\sqrt{2}$

60. $\sqrt{8}+\sqrt{18}$    a. $\sqrt{26}$    b. 13    c. $5\sqrt{2}$    d. can't simplify

61. $\left(3\sqrt{5}\right)^2$    a. $6\sqrt{5}$    b. $9\sqrt{5}$    c. 45    d. 225

62. If a typist can type "w" words in "m" minutes, what would be an expression for the number of words she could type in one minute?

   a. $w+m$    b. $w-m$    c. $wm$    d. $\dfrac{w}{m}$

63. How could you express the value in dollars of "d" dimes and "q" quarters?

   a. $q+d$    b. $25q+10d$    c. $0.25q+0.10d$    d. $35dq$

64. How could you express the value in cents of "d" dimes and "q" quarters?

   a. $q+d$    b. $25q+10d$    c. $0.25q+0.10d$    d. $35dq$

65. If the width of a rectangle is 5 less than its length, how could the area of the rectangle be expressed?

   a. $x-5$    b. $4x-10$    c. $x^2-5$    d. $x^2-5x$

66. A 25 foot plank is cut into two pieces. If one piece is "x" feet long, the other piece would be how long?

   a. $x-25$    b. $x+25$    c. $25-x$    d. $2x$

67. If "b" books cost "d" dollars, how much would "x" books cost?

   a. $dx$    b. $bdx$    c. $\dfrac{dx}{b}$    d. $\dfrac{bx}{d}$

68. The sum of three consecutive odd integers is 123. What are the integers?

   a. 40, 41, 42          b. 41, 43, 45          c. 39, 41, 43          d. 37, 41, 45

$$X + X+2 + X+4 = 123$$
$$3X + 6 = 123$$
$$-6$$
$$\frac{3X}{3} = \frac{117}{3}$$
$$X = 39$$

$$x = 39, 41, 43$$

69. The length of a rectangle is 3 ft more than 5 times its width. If the perimeter is 54 ft. What are the dimensions of the rectangle?

   a. 8 ft by 46 ft          b. 6 ft by 9 ft          c. 12 ft by 15 ft          d. 4 ft by 23 ft

70. A bus leaves its station at 1:00 p.m. and heads north at 55 mph. Two hours later a second bus leaves heading south at 60 mph. At what time will the buses be 340 miles apart?

   a. 3:00 pm          b. 4:00 pm          c. 5:00 pm          d. 6:00 pm

71. A biker rides out to the country. The trip takes 4 hours. The trip back takes 5 hours, but the rider drives 10 mph slower. How fast was the trip in each direction?

   a. 50 mph out, 40 mph back          b. 50 mph out, 60 mph back
   c. 40 mph out, 50 mph back          d. 60 mph out, 50 mph back

72. A bank contains 300 coins, all of them quarters or dimes. If the money totals $67.50, how many of each type of coin is in the bank?

   a. 250 quarters, 50 dimes          b. 50 quarters, 250 dimes
   c. 150 quarters, 150 dimes          d. 65 quarters, 235 dimes

73. Student tickets for a play cost $7 and non-student tickets cost $10. If 300 more students attend than non-students, and $8900 is raised, How many student tickets were purchased? Non-student tickets?

    a. 400 student, 700 non-student

    c. 400 student, 100 non-student

                      b. 700 student, 400 non-student

                      d. 400 student, 300 non-student

74. A lab has a 50% acid solution and a 20% acid solution. If they are to be mixed together to form 600mL of a 40% acid solution, how much of each should be used?

    a. 300 mL of 50%, 300mL of 20%

    c. 400 mL of 20%, 200mL of 50%

                      b. 200mL of 20%, 400mL of 50%

                      d. 300 mL 0f 50%, 120mL 0f 20%

$$x + y = 600$$

75. The area of a rectangle is 48 cm². If the width of the rectangle is 2 cm less than the length, what are the dimensions of the rectangle?

    a. 4 cm by 12 cm       b. 6 cm by 8 cm       c. –6 cm by 8 cm       d. 8cm by 10 cm

## Answers Comprehensive Review

| | | | | | | | | | |
|---|---|---|---|---|---|---|---|---|---|
| 1. c | 2. a | 3. a | 4. c | 5. d | 6. b | 7. c | 8. a | 9. a | 10. b |
| 11. d | 12. b | 13. c | 14. a | 15. c | 16. b | 17. b | 18. c | 19. b | 20. c |
| 21. d | 22. d | 23. c | 24. a | 25. b | 26. c | 27. d | 28. d | 29. b | 30. d |
| 31. c | 32. a | 33. d | 34. c | 35. b | 36. a | 37. c | 38. d | 39. b | 40. a |
| 41. d | 42. d | 43. c | 44. b | 45. c | 46. b | 47. b | 48. d | 49. c | 50. d |
| 51. d | 52. c | 53. d | 54. d | 55. b | 56. b | 57. a | 58. d | 59. d | 60. c |
| 61. c | 62. d | 63. c | 64. b | 65. d | 66. c | 67. c | 68. c | 69. d | 70. c |
| 71. a | 72. a | 73. b | 74. b | 75. b | | | | | |

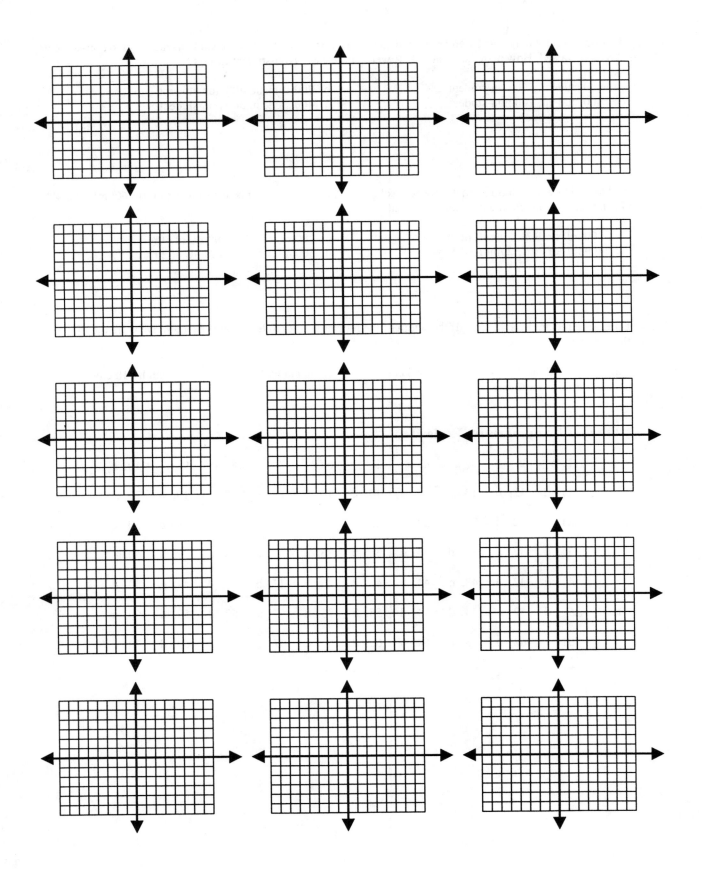